COMPLETE BOOK OF
Math
REPRODUCIBLES

Over 110 Activities for Today's Differentiated Classroom

Compiled by: Sara Inskeep
Cover design: Logo Design Team
Book Design: Jeff Richards

Printed in the United States of America

ISBN number: 978-1-4291-0459-3

MILLIKEN
P.O. Box 802 • Dayton, OH 45401
www.LorenzEducationalPress.com

How to Use This Book . . .

The activities in this book provide an excellent source of math practice for elementary students. The pages can be used as drill reinforcement or as independent instructional material and are designed to help motivate students to learn through a variety of exercises. The activities in this book are grouped by skill; these skills may overlap more than one grade level and should be used in ways that best meet each student's needs. The reproducibles are created so that a student can work with a minimum of supervision in a classroom or at home. Answer keys to all exercises have been provided in the back of the book.

EXTRA! EXTRA! When you see this symbol, be sure to check out the "extra" extension activity provided.

Table of Contents

Sensational Sums

Write each sum.

24 + 6 = ___	8 + 8 = ___	40 + 8 = ___	14 + 7 = ___
48 + 8 = ___	18 + 6 = ___	36 + 9 = ___	9 + 9 = ___

```
    7        9        7        3        5        9
    5        6        3        6        2        5
    4        6        0        6        5        7
    9        9        4        3        6        3
+   8    +   6    +   5    +   5    +   6    +   4
_____  _____  _____  _____  _____  _____


   34       57       95       71       27       19
   53       38       16       39       44       61
   97       88       37       93       28       37
+  84    +  24    +  91    +  36    +  55    +  24
_____  _____  _____  _____  _____  _____


   14       42       68       18       78       56
   29       29       25       54       89       49
   63       36       93       28       97       67
+  62    +  41    +  98    +  41    +  63    +  69
_____  _____  _____  _____  _____  _____
```

What is the total age of all the people who live in your house?

A Lot of Addition

Write each sum.

```
                                              317      249
                                              125      128
                                              256      751
                                           +  412   +  539
```

```
   799       159       527       858       438       900
   157       186       245       247       450       336
   283       292       741       509       426       862
 + 677     + 591     + 136     + 260     + 644     + 115
```

```
   588       591       997       725       512       243
   427       618       159       542       186       574
   590       922       328       147       829       307
 + 602     + 398     + 776     + 631     + 967     + 205
```

```
  3565      8759      9924      4885      9774
  7568      5264       517      5016      2828
 + 1458    + 1117    + 8666    + 8679    + 4132
```

```
  7709      9769      7801      2536      9117
  3615      7444      2976      1398      6279
 + 5524    + 1601    + 7801    + 8888    +  819
```

Add the average weights of an elephant, rhinoceros, and hippopotamus. How much would they weigh all together? (Use a book or other resource to find their weights.)

Adding Up the Answers

Across:

4. 14 + 26 + 34 + 12

6. 6 + 4 + 7 + 3 + 5

7. 4,729 + 8,219

9. 16 + 18 + 13 + 15

11. 89 + 92 + 97

12. 19 + 22 + 24 + 23

14. 7 + 4 + 5 + 2 + 6

15. 22 + 19 + 17 + 18

17. 20 + 22 + 23 + 17

19. 24 + 22 + 23 + 28

20. 18 + 16 + 20 + 21

22. 178 + 181 + 169 + 193

23. 18 + 17 + 14 + 13

24. 18,028 + 10,425

26. 21 + 19 + 23 + 26

27. 14 + 18 + 15 + 21

Down:

1. 23 + 26 + 28 + 21

2. 2,027 + 2,069

3. 33 + 16 + 22 + 14

5. 23 + 13 + 10 + 15

6. 4 + 7 + 2 + 6 + 9

8. 19,928 + 22,257

10. 70,108 + 50,706

13. 8 + 9 + 7 + 6 + 7

14. 74 + 68 + 81 + 75

16. 159 + 162 + 149 + 177

18. 102,208 + 104,870

19. 21 + 18 + 20 + 31

21. 9,894 + 11,231

23. 3,027 + 3,456

24. 6 + 5 + 7 + 4 + 7

25. 7 + 8 + 6 + 9 + 6

26. 27 + 29 + 28

28. 18 + 20 + 16 + 26

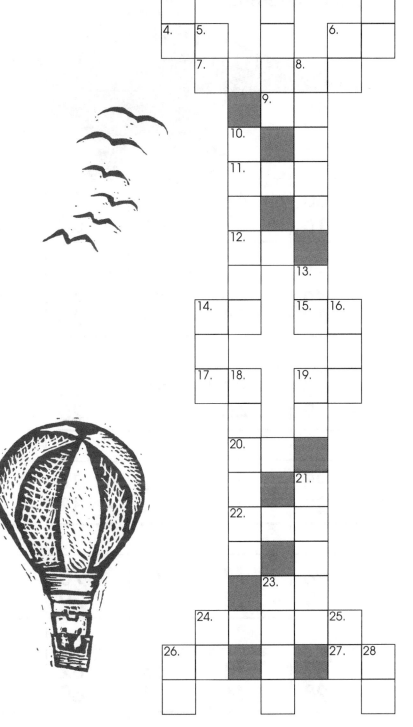

Subtraction Solutions

Write each difference.

45 − 17				50 − 25	74 − 47	81 − 48
60 − 16	65 − 47	73 − 44	61 − 52	84 − 36	80 − 61	35 − 16
98 − 19	66 − 18	94 − 39	71 − 35	64 − 39	92 − 67	72 − 24
90 − 79	93 − 45	90 − 13	52 − 25	76 − 17	76 − 38	70 − 58
95 − 29	51 − 36	50 − 34	74 − 37	95 − 38	80 − 48	92 − 53
96 − 59	77 − 18	71 − 24	70 − 29	82 − 59	63 − 24	81 − 13
82 − 28	73 − 46	63 − 48	82 − 69	81 − 59	84 − 38	56 − 17
98 − 79	70 − 17	80 − 12	62 − 36	46 − 29	81 − 47	

Subtractosaurs

Write each difference.

22 − 20	97 − 96	28 − 11	66 − 65	76 − 25	49 − 31	59 − 34
81 − 40	92 − 81	68 − 32	99 − 48	50 − 30	97 − 33	88 − 36
79 − 49	67 − 47	98 − 65	52 − 42	69 − 36	56 − 50	88 − 75
96 − 72	78 − 58	96 − 74	85 − 31	55 − 13	98 − 90	47 − 12
67 − 14	49 − 36	95 − 45	18 − 13	33 − 30		
83 − 63	77 − 45	84 − 12	98 − 14	96 − 26	97 − 81	84 − 80

EXTRA! Find the difference in your age and the age of your grandmother or grandfather.

Subtraction Rodeo

Write each difference.

			8 3 4 5 − 1 8 4 7	2 7 3 2 − 1 7 7 6
4 0 3 2 − 2 6 7 5			1 6 2 3 − 7 6 6	7 0 0 0 − 3 7 7 5
3 9 8 7 − 2 9 9 8	3 0 4 7 − 1 2 9 9	9 8 7 6 − 3 8 7 7	6 0 0 0 − 5 8 8 8	7 2 0 2 − 1 3 7 3
8 4 0 0 − 5 6 1 9	2 2 0 5 − 5 7 8	6 6 6 8 − 1 7 7 9	5 6 4 5 − 3 7 5 4	3 0 5 2 − 1 6 6 3
9 4 0 0 − 4 5 2 4	9 0 9 0 − 6 9 5	4 0 0 1 − 5 4 2	3 2 1 0 − 1 0 2 3	6 0 1 1 − 1 3 3 0
4 0 0 5 − 1 5 2 3	3 7 3 6 − 8 4 5	5 1 7 1 − 2 2 4 5	7 8 7 5 − 1 5 8 8	4 0 4 0 − 2 4 4 1
1 2 3 7 − 1 1 7 8	1 7 2 5 − 8 3 5	3 6 3 2 − 2 5 7 5	9 1 9 1 − 5 2 5 3	6 4 0 9 − 3 7 5 9

Ask your Mom or Dad what year they graduated high school. Use that information, along with their age, to determine how old he or she was on graduation day.

Name_____ Date_____

Deep-Sea Subtraction

Across:

7. (97 – 19) – 14
9. (93 – 17) – (72 – 57)
11. 24,032 – 12,016
12. (83 –16) – (61 – 22)
13. (72 – 16) – (63 – 36)
14. (95 – 16) – 37
16. 408 – 112

17. 880 – 459
18. (92 – 14) – (42 – 13)
19. 20,458 – 20,164
20. 905 – 280
22. 8639 – 4813
24. 42,640 – 20,905

28. 5,218 – 3,054
31. (90 – 13) – 31
32. 61,299 – 29,111
33. 57,209 – 33,072
34. (96 – 27) – 31

Down:

1. (82 – 18) – (71 – 33)
2. (98 – 19) – 43
3. 602 – 186
4. 811 – 547
5. (94 – 15) – (50 – 39)
6. (66 –19) – (62 – 34)
8. (100 – 12) – 44
10. 318,081 – 194,019

12. 432,846 – 216,423
13. (87 – 19) – 39
15. 6,409 – 4,191
18. 9,078 – 4,562
21. (86 – 17) – (80 – 28)
22. (94 – 19) – 39
23. 472 – 236
24. 996 – 706

25. (84 – 19) – (75 – 28)
26. (96 – 18) – 46
27. 1,088 – 544
29. 812 – 633
30. (84 –18) – (72 – 49)
31. (93 –18) – 27
35. (100 –11) – (62 – 55)

Major Multiplication

Write each product.

```
        5732
      x  276
       34392  →    6 x 5732
      401240  →   70 x 5732
     1146400  →  200 x 5732
     1,582,032
```

Multiplication (by a three-digit factor)

$$\begin{array}{r} 852 \\ \times\ 647 \\ \hline \end{array} \qquad \begin{array}{r} 240 \\ \times\ 487 \\ \hline \end{array}$$

$$\begin{array}{r} 308 \\ \times\ 502 \\ \hline \end{array} \qquad \begin{array}{r} 456 \\ \times\ 733 \\ \hline \end{array}$$

$$\begin{array}{r} 5000 \\ \times\ 800 \\ \hline \end{array} \quad \begin{array}{r} 6004 \\ \times\ 454 \\ \hline \end{array} \quad \begin{array}{r} 6042 \\ \times\ 455 \\ \hline \end{array} \quad \begin{array}{r} 6603 \\ \times\ 706 \\ \hline \end{array}$$

$$\begin{array}{r} 2843 \\ \times\ 381 \\ \hline \end{array} \quad \begin{array}{r} 1026 \\ \times\ 967 \\ \hline \end{array} \quad \begin{array}{r} 3050 \\ \times\ 715 \\ \hline \end{array} \quad \begin{array}{r} 5732 \\ \times\ 276 \\ \hline \end{array}$$

$$\begin{array}{r} 9111 \\ \times\ 637 \\ \hline \end{array} \quad \begin{array}{r} 5916 \\ \times\ 194 \\ \hline \end{array} \quad \begin{array}{r} 1206 \\ \times\ 199 \\ \hline \end{array} \quad \begin{array}{r} 8565 \\ \times\ 703 \\ \hline \end{array}$$

More Multiplication

Write each product.

$$3402 \times 54$$

$$
\begin{array}{r}
213 \\
\times 128 \\
\hline
1704 \rightarrow \quad 8 \times 213 \\
4260 \rightarrow \quad 20 \times 213 \\
21300 \rightarrow \quad 100 \times 213 \\
\hline
27,264
\end{array}
$$

Multiplication (by a two- or three-digit factor)

$$7894 \times 30$$

$$6600 \times 25$$

$$2000 \times 70$$

$$3768 \times 67$$

$$1123 \times 16$$

$$2009 \times 99$$

$$522 \times 375$$

$$168 \times 747$$

$$900 \times 680$$

$$359 \times 274$$

$$405 \times 436$$

$$640 \times 519$$

$$213 \times 128$$

$$837 \times 702$$

Find a snack that has 100 or more calories per serving. How many calories would you take in if you ate 5 servings of that snack?

Multiplication Puzzler

Across:

3. 24 x 36

7. (25 x 17) – (12 x 28)

8. (18 x 21) – (103 x 3)

10. (12 x 29) – (91 x 3)

11. (4 x 15) + (14 x 2)

13. (14 x 15) – (19 x 9)

14. 28 x 35

15. 13 x 62

16. (25 x 22) – (29 x 16)

18. 8 x 371

20. 24 x 121

22. (26 x 11) – (2 x 97)

25. (19 x 21) – (101 x 3)

26. 61 x 11

28. (12 x 31) – (25 x 12)

30. (14 x 4) + (14 x 3)

32. 44 x 19

34. 491 x 12

35. 18 x 53

36. 401 x 22

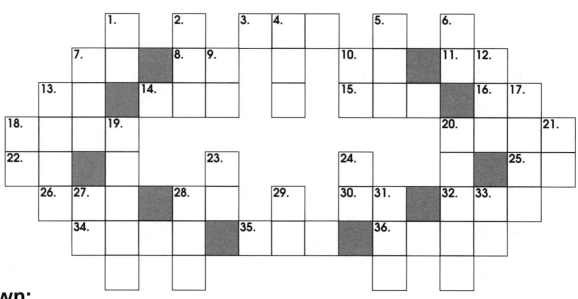

Down:

1. (4 x 13) + (9 x 3)

2. 32 x 24

4. 23 x 27

5. 38 x 25

6. (26 x 32) – (31 x 24)

7. 28 x 32

9. (23 x 16) – (2 x 139)

10. (16 x 3) + (15 x 2)

12. 7 x 127

13. 13 x 302

17. 1,524 x 4

18. (28 x 20) – (9x 59)

19. 929 x 96

20. 116 x 214

21. (24 x 16) – (2 x 169)

23. (19 x 3) + (7 x 5)

24. (19 x 26) – (25 x 17)

27. (12 x 13) – (27 x 3)

28. 52 x 14

29. (27 x 12) – (9 x 31)

31. 17 x 52

33. (14 x 24) – (16 x 19)

Multiplication Galaxy

Across:

3. 21 x 45

7. (13 x 4) + (2 x 23)

8. (3 x 31) – (13 x 5)

10. (19 x 3) + (2 x 19)

11. (5 x 13) + (16 x 2)

13. (11 x 11) – (18 x 6)

14. 50 x 19

15. 129 x 7

16. (15 x 13) – (28 x 4)

18. 341 x 4

20. 103 x 23

22. (16 x 4) + (2 x 13)

25. (13 x 13) – (5 x 15)

26. 64 x 15

28. (81 x 5) – (65 x 5)

30. (23 x 2) + (8 x 4)

32. 16 x 56

34. 391 x 13

35. 18 x 52

36. 402 x 21

Down:

1. (19 x 5) – (9 x 3)

2. 35 x 15

4. 15 x 33

5. 34 x 25

6. (21 x 3) + (18 x 2)

7. 26 x 36

9. (14 x 15) – (2 x 65)

10. (3 x 17) + (16 x 3)

12. 29 x 27

13. 119 x 11

17. 462 x 8

18. (19 x 9) – (19 x 8)

19. 875 x 56

20. 1,678 x 16

21. (16 x 21) – (22 x 11)

23. (17 x 10) – (5 x 22)

24. (16 x 8) – (7 x 13)

27. (6 x 19) – (7 x 7)

28. 27 x 31

29. (9 x 16) – (3 x 27)

31. 16 x 55

33. (8 x 5) + (26 x 2)

Math Lab

Help the scientist make the number cells grow.
Write the missing factors.

Circle the prime numbers.

53   34   79   7   41   44   53   71   92   99

14

The Math Artist

Shade the regions that contain factors of 72.

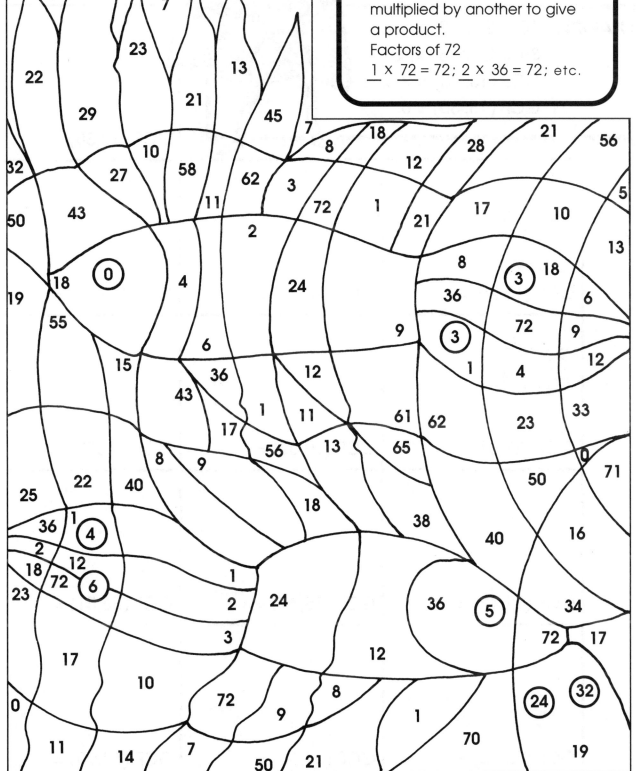

A factor is a number that is multiplied by another to give a product.
Factors of 72
1 x 72 = 72; 2 x 36 = 72; etc.

The Mathematician

Write the greatest common factor
for each pair of numbers.

EXAMPLE: 18 = 2 x 3 x 3
30 = 2 x 3 x 5
GCF (18, 30) = 2 x 3
GCF (18, 30) = 6

GCF (18,30) =

GCF (15,25) =	GCF (24,32) =	GCF (20,28) =
GCF (27,81) =	GCF (39,52) =	GCF (9,57) =
GCF (12,42) =	GCF (35,49) =	GCF (36,51) =
GCF (32,48) =	GCF (54,66) =	GCF (63,90) =

16

Fun with Factors

Write the greatest common factor (GCF) of each pair of numbers.

GCF(4,6)
Factors of 4 are ①, ②, 4.
Factors of 6 are ①, ②, 3, 6.
Greatest common factor of 4 and 6 is 2.
GCF(4,6) = 2.

GCF(4,6)   = _____

GCF(8,15)   = _____

GCF(9,24)   = _____

GCF(16,36) = _____

GCF(8,12)   = _____

GCF(3,27)   = _____

GCF(10,22) = _____

GCF(15,35) = _____

GCF(14,21) = _____

GCF(18,30) = _____

GCF(10,25) = _____

GCF(20,32) = _____

GCF(7,21)   = _____

Multiple Mania

Write the least common multiple (LCM) of each pair of numbers.

LCM(4,6)
Multiples of 4 are ⓪, 4 , 8 , ⑫, 16 , 20...
Multiples of 6 are ⓪, 6 , ⑫, 18 , 24 , 30...
Zero is never used as a least common multiple.
The least common multiple of 4 and 6 is 12.
LCM(4,6) = 12.

LCM(4,6)   = _____

LCM(3,10) = _____	LCM(3,4) = _____	LCM(6,7) = _____
LCM(8,12) = _____	LCM(6,8) = _____	LCM(8,10) = _____
LCM(2,5) = _____	LCM(2,3) = _____	LCM(4,5) = _____
LCM(5,6) = _____	LCM(3,9) = _____	LCM(5,7) = _____

Multiple Mania

Write the least common multiple for each pair of numbers.

LCM (9,12) =	**EXAMPLE:** 9 = 3 x 3 12 = 3 x 2 x 2 LCM (9, 12) = 3 x 3 x 2 x 2 LCM (9, 12) = 36

LCM (6,10) =	LCM (12,16) =	LCM (14,20) =
LCM (8,36) =	LCM (15,27) =	LCM (5,9) =
LCM (11,22) =	LCM (18,24) =	LCM (4,22) =
LCM (15,25) =	LCM (28,35) =	LCM (21,30) =

Quotient Questions

Write each quotient.

4)92

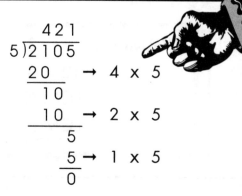

```
      421
5)2105
   20      → 4 x 5
   10
   10      → 2 x 5
    5
    5   → 1 x 5
    0
```

Division (one-digit divisors)

2)38

6)78

8)96

5)65   7)91   3)93   9)90   2)56   3)87

9)189   6)684   3)210   8)424   6)804

5)5050   7)4340   8)1696   6)1320   5)2105

Use a box of cereal to find out how many servings are in one box. Hint: use division.

Double-Digit Division

Write each quotient.

```
      83
 29)2407
    232    → 8 × 29
     87
     87    → 3 × 29
      0
```
Division (two-digit divisors)

36)864   70)700

53)901   24)984   27)918   30)930

44)924   65)845   51)5151   87)9570

31)3658   48)3216   16)5152   29)2407

Dino Division

Divide. Check by multiplication.

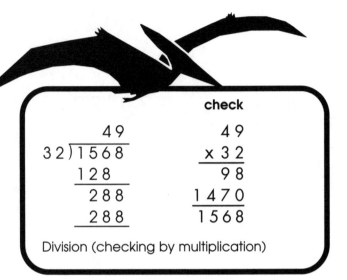

```
         49        check
              49
  32)1568    x 32
     128        98
     288      1470
     288      1568
```

Division (checking by multiplication)

Check

```
  32)1568
```

x _____

Check

```
  62)4836
```

x _____

```
  71)6532
```

x _____

```
  81)25,758
```

x _____

```
  59)37,170
```

x _____

```
  95)51,965
```

x _____

```
  23)20,907
```

x _____

Divide and Conquer

Across:

3. 3,888 ÷ 9
5. 3,316 ÷ 4
6. 121 ÷ 11
7. 3,060 ÷ 5
10. 2,124 ÷ 6
11. 1,338 ÷ 3
12. 475 ÷ 25
13. 2,864 ÷ 4
16. 1,089 ÷ 9
17. 1,981 ÷ 7
18. 378 ÷ 14
19. 1,584 ÷ 8
22. 1,485 ÷ 9
23. 3,794 ÷ 7
24. 990 ÷ 33
25. 2,512 ÷ 8
28. 4,260 ÷ 6
29. 2,664 ÷ 12
31. 846 ÷ 9
32. 497 ÷ 7
35. 720 ÷ 40
36. 836 ÷ 22
38. 376 ÷ 8
39. 534 ÷ 6

Down:

1. 1,136 ÷ 8
2. 924 ÷ 22
4. 468 ÷ 12
5. 2,448 ÷ 3
8. 1,206 ÷ 9
9. 1,792 ÷ 7
11. 1,988 ÷ 4
14. 1,298 ÷ 11
15. 3,115 ÷ 5
17. 2,439 ÷ 9
20. 2,742 ÷ 3
21. 3,448 ÷ 4
23. 4,024 ÷ 8
26. 1,548 ÷ 9
27. 8,254 ÷ 2
29. 576 ÷ 24
30. 686 ÷ 7
31. 2,961 ÷ 3
33. 888 ÷ 6
34. 704 ÷ 8
35. 400 ÷ 25
37. 594 ÷ 6
40. 1,820 ÷ 20

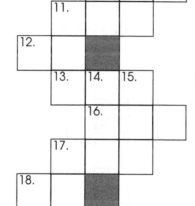

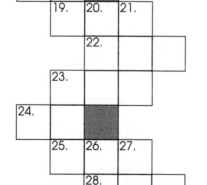

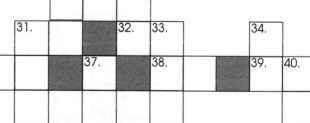

Name_____   Date_____

Dare to Divide

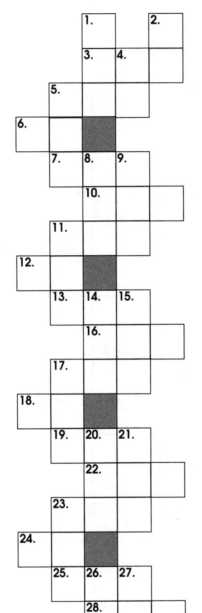

Across:

3. 4,347 ÷ 7
5. 2,376 ÷ 9
6. 924 ÷ 14
7. 3,091 ÷ 11
10. 3,908 ÷ 4
11. 2,190 ÷ 15
12. 988 ÷ 26
13. 4,984 ÷ 8
16. 3,744 ÷ 9
17. 3,510 ÷ 18
18. 1,274 ÷ 13
19. 5,922 ÷ 6
22. 2,028 ÷ 12
23. 3,920 ÷ 16
24. 987 ÷ 21
25. 2,912 ÷ 7
28. 6,456 ÷ 8
29. 5,731 ÷ 11
31. 988 ÷ 38
32. 696 ÷ 29
35. 1,200 ÷ 25
36. 1,992 ÷ 24
38. 972 ÷ 12
39. 1,900 ÷ 20

Down:

1. 3,486 ÷ 21
2. 682 ÷ 22
4. 792 ÷ 33
5. 2,096 ÷ 8
8. 6,258 ÷ 7
9. 2,112 ÷ 12
11. 2,976 ÷ 16
14. 2,241 ÷ 9
15. 3,465 ÷ 11
17. 2,646 ÷ 14
20. 6,512 ÷ 8
21. 4,590 ÷ 6
23. 4,110 ÷ 15
26. 4,550 ÷ 25
27. 18,036 ÷ 3
29. 952 ÷ 17
30. 884 ÷ 13
31. 1,673 ÷ 7
33. 1,932 ÷ 4
34. 828 ÷ 12
35. 1,175 ÷ 25
37. 609 ÷ 29
40. 1,368 ÷ 24

Name _____ Date _____

Fraction Flavors

Refresh your memory on three kinds of fractions. Label (or shade) the ice cream cones below with the correct color.

$\frac{1}{2}, \frac{9}{12}, \frac{6}{8}, \frac{3}{5}$
(vanilla–white)
Proper Fractions

$\frac{2}{2}, \frac{8}{4}, \frac{12}{5}, \frac{10}{6}$
(strawberry–red)
Improper Fractions

$1\frac{1}{2}, 9\frac{3}{10}, 3\frac{4}{5}$
Mixed Numbers
(chocolate–brown)

A.  $4\frac{1}{2}$ $\frac{3}{3}$  $\frac{14}{17}$

B. 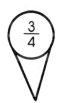 $\frac{3}{4}$ $6\frac{1}{8}$ $\frac{30}{10}$

C. $\frac{1}{2}$ $8\frac{3}{10}$ $\frac{16}{8}$ $8\frac{2}{3}$ $4\frac{1}{5}$  $\frac{2}{3}$

Write the following improper fractions as whole numbers or as mixed numbers. Write your answers on the cones.

D.  $\frac{17}{8}$  $\frac{14}{3}$  $\frac{11}{9}$  $\frac{25}{6}$  $\frac{4}{4}$  $\frac{18}{9}$  $\frac{22}{7}$ $\frac{9}{8}$

Now, rename these mixed numbers as improper fractions.

E.  $4\frac{1}{2}$  $5\frac{2}{3}$  $6\frac{3}{5}$  $2\frac{5}{8}$  $6\frac{1}{7}$  $3\frac{3}{10}$  $6\frac{4}{6}$  $1\frac{2}{5}$

Picturing Fractions

Shade fractions in their simplest form.

EXAMPLE:

$$\frac{9}{12} = \frac{9}{12} \div \frac{3}{3} = \frac{3}{4}$$

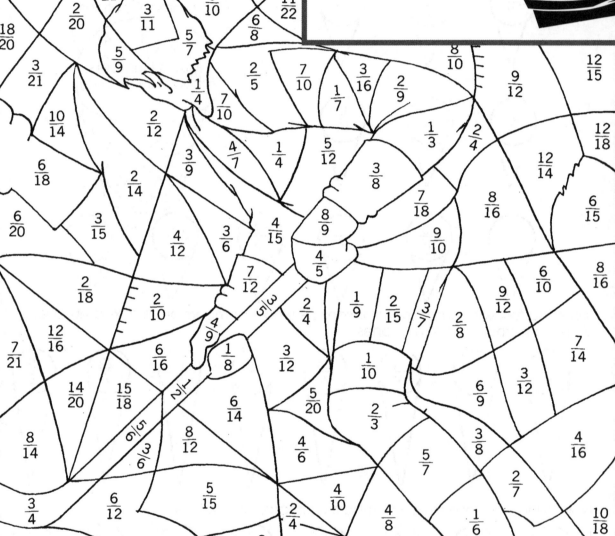

The Math Map

Shade all fractions in simplest form. Rewrite the unshaded fractions in simplest form.

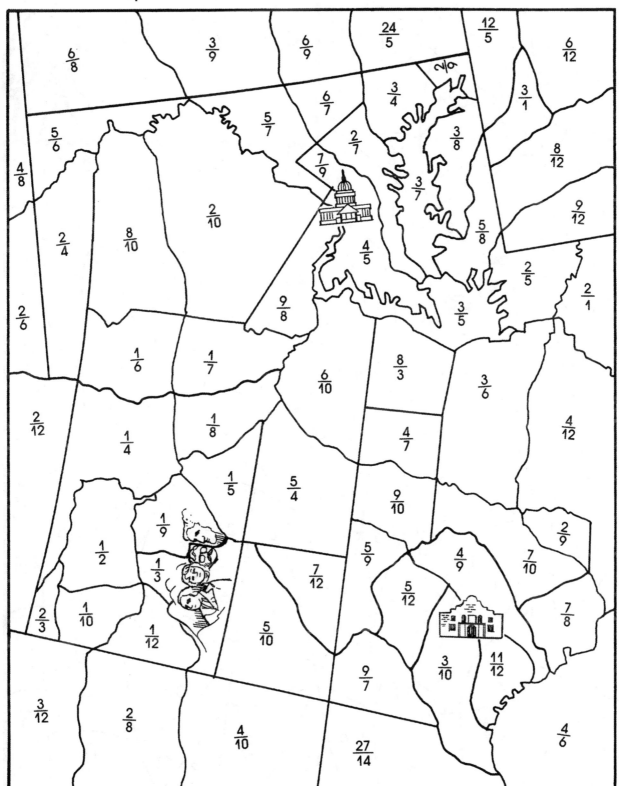

Picturing Fractions

Shade in all mixed numerals in their simplest form.

EXAMPLE:

$$6\frac{12}{9} = 7\frac{3}{9} = 7\frac{1}{3}$$

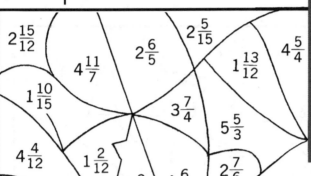

$2\frac{15}{12}$ $4\frac{11}{7}$ $2\frac{6}{5}$ $2\frac{5}{15}$ $1\frac{13}{12}$ $4\frac{5}{4}$

$1\frac{10}{15}$ $3\frac{7}{4}$ $5\frac{5}{3}$

$4\frac{4}{12}$ $1\frac{2}{12}$ $3\frac{3}{2}$ $4\frac{6}{10}$ $2\frac{7}{6}$

$3\frac{3}{9}$ $1\frac{7}{8}$ $1\frac{5}{7}$ $3\frac{9}{4}$ $2\frac{8}{10}$ $3\frac{2}{10}$ $2\frac{10}{12}$ $4\frac{8}{5}$

$4\frac{2}{5}$ $2\frac{4}{9}$ $3\frac{3}{10}$ $1\frac{3}{6}$ $2\frac{11}{10}$ $1\frac{1}{4}$ $1\frac{2}{14}$

$4\frac{8}{5}$ $1\frac{10}{9}$ $2\frac{2}{4}$ $2\frac{10}{7}$ $1\frac{7}{10}$ $1\frac{12}{8}$

$2\frac{4}{14}$ $2\frac{1}{4}$ $2\frac{1}{6}$ $1\frac{4}{3}$ $1\frac{4}{6}$ $2\frac{3}{7}$ $3\frac{9}{8}$

$2\frac{12}{9}$ $2\frac{1}{6}$ $1\frac{5}{9}$ $2\frac{12}{19}$ $1\frac{7}{12}$ $2\frac{7}{9}$ $1\frac{1}{3}$ $2\frac{2}{6}$

$1\frac{6}{4}$ $2\frac{7}{5}$ $1\frac{1}{12}$ $1\frac{1}{4}$ $5\frac{5}{12}$ $3\frac{1}{7}$ $2\frac{3}{8}$ $2\frac{4}{5}$ $2\frac{5}{10}$

$1\frac{6}{12}$ $3\frac{6}{7}$ $2\frac{1}{10}$ $3\frac{1}{5}$ $1\frac{1}{9}$ $1\frac{10}{6}$

$3\frac{2}{8}$ $1\frac{1}{3}$ $3\frac{5}{8}$ $1\frac{1}{2}$ $2\frac{4}{7}$ $2\frac{4}{15}$ $3\frac{8}{16}$

$2\frac{15}{12}$ $4\frac{8}{9}$ $3\frac{2}{9}$ $2\frac{7}{6}$ $2\frac{6}{8}$ $4\frac{4}{7}$ $3\frac{2}{3}$ $2\frac{13}{10}$

$1\frac{6}{9}$ $4\frac{8}{6}$ $4\frac{9}{7}$ $5\frac{9}{12}$ $1\frac{4}{10}$ $1\frac{1}{8}$ $3\frac{3}{2}$

$2\frac{9}{15}$ $2\frac{10}{8}$ $1\frac{2}{7}$ $1\frac{5}{6}$ $2\frac{9}{5}$ $1\frac{3}{4}$

$3\frac{9}{6}$ $1\frac{4}{8}$ $1\frac{13}{12}$ $3\frac{3}{15}$ $5\frac{11}{8}$

$1\frac{12}{15}$ $1\frac{3}{5}$ $1\frac{12}{10}$

$3\frac{9}{8}$ $1\frac{4}{16}$ $1\frac{10}{6}$ $5\frac{3}{12}$ $2\frac{7}{5}$ $4\frac{11}{9}$ $2\frac{2}{16}$

Fractions in Disguise

Write each mixed number as a fraction.

$$2\frac{5}{12} = \frac{2}{1} + \frac{5}{12} = \frac{24}{12} + \frac{5}{12} = \frac{29}{12}$$

Mixed numerals (renaming)

$3\frac{7}{12} = \frac{}{12}$	$8\frac{3}{4} = \frac{}{4}$
$5\frac{1}{7} = \frac{}{7}$	$9\frac{5}{7} = \frac{}{7}$

$4\frac{1}{5} = \frac{}{5}$	$10\frac{3}{5} = \frac{}{5}$	$3\frac{3}{4} = \frac{}{4}$	$4\frac{3}{8} = \frac{}{8}$
$10\frac{2}{3} = \frac{}{3}$	$3\frac{3}{10} = \frac{}{10}$	$8\frac{6}{7} = \frac{}{7}$	$1\frac{2}{5} = \frac{}{5}$
$5\frac{1}{2} = \frac{}{2}$	$6\frac{1}{3} = \frac{}{3}$	$1\frac{1}{6} = \frac{}{6}$	$6\frac{5}{8} = \frac{}{8}$
$4\frac{5}{6} = \frac{}{6}$	$5\frac{2}{3} = \frac{}{3}$	$3\frac{1}{3} = \frac{}{3}$	$7\frac{1}{2} = \frac{}{2}$
$6\frac{3}{5} =$	$5\frac{8}{9} =$	$10\frac{1}{2} =$	$4\frac{4}{5} =$
$10\frac{3}{8} =$	$8\frac{1}{6} =$	$2\frac{9}{10} =$	$2\frac{3}{7} =$
$6\frac{11}{12} =$	$5\frac{5}{12} =$	$7\frac{7}{10} =$	$5\frac{3}{8} =$
$6\frac{1}{4} =$	$3\frac{1}{7} =$	$4\frac{1}{8} =$	$5\frac{5}{12} =$

EXTRA!

Write the name of an item that is commonly measured in fractions.

Math Hive

Write each fraction as a mixed number or whole number.

$\frac{9}{8}$ =			$\frac{8}{5}$ =
$\frac{35}{5}$ =			$\frac{77}{8}$ =
$\frac{7}{2}$ =	$\frac{96}{8}$ =	$\frac{63}{9}$ =	$\frac{25}{9}$ =
$\frac{10}{2}$ =	$\frac{13}{4}$ =	$\frac{15}{8}$ =	$\frac{10}{10}$ =
$\frac{33}{11}$ =	$\frac{56}{5}$ =	$\frac{19}{6}$ =	$\frac{52}{4}$ =
$\frac{56}{7}$ =	$\frac{43}{3}$ =	$\frac{73}{11}$ =	$\frac{37}{12}$ =
$\frac{17}{10}$ =	$\frac{54}{9}$ =	$\frac{16}{9}$ =	$\frac{21}{4}$ =
$\frac{21}{8}$ =	$\frac{65}{7}$ =	$\frac{36}{12}$ =	$\frac{15}{3}$ =
$\frac{51}{4}$ =	$\frac{21}{2}$ =	$\frac{66}{11}$ =	$\frac{30}{3}$ =
$\frac{18}{3}$ =	$\frac{20}{9}$ =	$\frac{19}{12}$ =	$\frac{13}{6}$ =

$$\frac{21}{8} = 21 \div 8 = 2\frac{5}{8}$$

Fractions (renaming)

Find the origin of the word **fraction**. Use a dictionary or other resource to help you.

The Math Detective

1. Using the numbers 1, 5, 6, 7, fill in the boxes below to form two fractions whose sum is as close to 1 as possible, but not 1. Each number may be used only once.

$$\frac{\square}{\square} + \frac{\square}{\square} \ =$$

2. Using the numbers 2, 5, 6, 8, fill in the boxes below to form two fractions whose sum is as close to 1 as possible, but not less than 1. Each number may only be used once.

$$\frac{\square}{\square} + \frac{\square}{\square} \ =$$

3. Using the numbers 3, 5, 7, 9, fill in the boxes below to form two fractions whose sum is greater than 2. Each number may only be used once.

$$\frac{\square}{\square} + \frac{\square}{\square} \ =$$

4. Using the numbers 2, 4, 6, 8, fill in the boxes below to form two fractions whose sum is greater than 3. Each number may be used only once.

$$\frac{\square}{\square} + \frac{\square}{\square} \ =$$

5. Using the numbers 1, 2, 15, 16, fill in the boxes below to form two fractions whose sum is as close to 0 as possible. Each number may be used only once.

$$\frac{\square}{\square} + \frac{\square}{\square} \ =$$

Keep It Simple

Write each sum in simplest form.

$\frac{3}{5} + \frac{4}{5} =$	$\frac{9}{12} + \frac{10}{12} =$	

$$\frac{4}{15} + \frac{1}{15} = \frac{4+1}{15} = \frac{5}{15} = \frac{1}{3}$$

Addition of fractional numbers
(like denominators)

$\frac{5}{8} + \frac{1}{8} =$	$\frac{7}{15} + \frac{8}{15} =$		
$\frac{4}{5} + \frac{2}{5} =$	$\frac{2}{17} + \frac{2}{17} =$	$\frac{5}{10} + \frac{2}{10} =$	$\frac{5}{15} + \frac{8}{15} =$
$\frac{4}{11} + \frac{4}{11} =$	$\frac{6}{9} + \frac{3}{9} =$	$\frac{3}{4} + \frac{3}{4} =$	$\frac{5}{11} + \frac{8}{11} =$
$\frac{2}{4} + \frac{3}{4} =$	$\frac{4}{10} + \frac{1}{10} =$	$\frac{7}{14} + \frac{4}{14} =$	$\frac{3}{12} + \frac{4}{12} =$
$\frac{5}{10} + \frac{4}{10} =$	$\frac{1}{9} + \frac{6}{9} =$	$\frac{4}{15} + \frac{1}{15} =$	$\frac{4}{15} + \frac{13}{15} =$
$\frac{11}{12} + \frac{5}{12} =$	$\frac{7}{8} + \frac{7}{8} =$	$\frac{3}{8} + \frac{5}{8} =$	$\frac{5}{9} + \frac{8}{9} =$
$\frac{11}{22} + \frac{4}{22} =$	$\frac{2}{8} + \frac{5}{8} =$	$\frac{3}{7} + \frac{3}{7} =$	$\frac{7}{15} + \frac{4}{15} =$
$\frac{4}{25} + \frac{8}{25} =$	$\frac{6}{8} + \frac{7}{8} =$	$\frac{3}{10} + \frac{5}{10} =$	$\frac{5}{12} + \frac{5}{12} =$
$\frac{1}{6} + \frac{3}{6} =$	$\frac{3}{7} + \frac{6}{7} =$	$\frac{4}{8} + \frac{1}{8} =$	$\frac{9}{12} + \frac{2}{12} =$

Add the fraction of kids in your class who like rock music to the fraction of kids who like country music.

Funky Fractions

Add the following unlike fractions.

1. $\frac{2}{12} + \frac{1}{4} =$

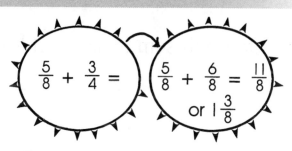

$\frac{5}{8} + \frac{3}{4} =$ $\frac{5}{8} + \frac{6}{8} = \frac{11}{8}$ or $1\frac{3}{8}$

2. $\frac{5}{10} + \frac{2}{3} =$

3. $\frac{1}{4} + \frac{10}{16} =$

4. $\frac{6}{10} + \frac{1}{2} =$

5. $\frac{4}{8} + \frac{6}{10} =$

6. $\frac{14}{60} + \frac{1}{2} =$

7. $\frac{1}{5} + \frac{2}{10} =$

8. $\frac{1}{4} + \frac{12}{24} =$

9. $\frac{1}{6} + \frac{2}{18} =$

10. $\frac{13}{5} + \frac{6}{15} =$

11. $\frac{5}{25} + \frac{7}{5} =$

12. $\frac{1}{12} + \frac{1}{4} =$

13. $\frac{10}{35} + \frac{2}{7} =$

14. $\frac{20}{40} + \frac{1}{2} =$

15. $\frac{16}{20} + \frac{2}{5} =$

Total Awesome Score

Simple Sums

Write each sum in simplest form.

$\dfrac{11}{12}$ = —— + $\dfrac{1}{3}$ = ——	$\dfrac{3}{5}$ = —— + $\dfrac{4}{15}$ = ——	

$$\begin{array}{r} \dfrac{3}{4} = \dfrac{9}{12} \\[4pt] + \dfrac{1}{12} = + \dfrac{1}{12} \\[2pt] \hline \dfrac{10}{12} = \dfrac{5}{6} \end{array}$$

Addition of fractional numbers
(unlike denominators)

$\dfrac{3}{10}$ = —— + $\dfrac{4}{5}$ = ——	$\dfrac{3}{4}$ = —— + $\dfrac{1}{12}$ = ——	$\dfrac{1}{6}$ = —— + $\dfrac{1}{2}$ = ——

$\dfrac{5}{6}$ = —— + $\dfrac{5}{18}$ = ——	$\dfrac{2}{9}$ = —— + $\dfrac{2}{3}$ = ——	$\dfrac{3}{4}$ = —— + $\dfrac{7}{16}$ = ——	$\dfrac{4}{5}$ = —— + $\dfrac{7}{10}$ = ——
$\dfrac{1}{16}$ = —— + $\dfrac{7}{8}$ = ——	$\dfrac{1}{2}$ = —— + $\dfrac{1}{8}$ = ——	$\dfrac{2}{3}$ = —— + $\dfrac{7}{15}$ = ——	$\dfrac{2}{3}$ = —— + $\dfrac{5}{12}$ = ——
$\dfrac{5}{14}$ = —— + $\dfrac{3}{7}$ = ——	$\dfrac{5}{6}$ = —— + $\dfrac{1}{3}$ = ——	$\dfrac{1}{18}$ = —— + $\dfrac{4}{9}$ = ——	$\dfrac{3}{4}$ = —— + $\dfrac{1}{2}$ = ——

Parts and Wholes

Write each sum.

$11 \frac{5}{6}$ + 8	12 + $6 \frac{5}{8}$	$11 \frac{3}{4}$ + 4		
23 + $3 \frac{4}{5}$	$5 \frac{1}{10}$ + 21	$6 \frac{9}{10}$ + 8		
$10 \frac{2}{3}$ + 2	$25 \frac{1}{8}$ + 3	5 + $7 \frac{3}{5}$	7 + $9 \frac{3}{10}$	20 + $5 \frac{1}{2}$
$8 \frac{1}{2}$ + 3	$8 \frac{2}{7}$ + 4	$15 \frac{1}{3}$ + 9	6 + $4 \frac{1}{5}$	12 + $5 \frac{3}{7}$

20
$+ 5 \frac{1}{2}$
$\overline{25 \frac{1}{2}}$

Addition of mixed numbers and whole numbers

$18 + 7 \frac{1}{4} =$	$31 + 3 \frac{1}{6} =$	$23 + 6 \frac{7}{8} =$
$15 \frac{1}{3} + 5 =$	$30 \frac{2}{3} + 7 =$	$26 + 9 \frac{1}{5} =$
$22 \frac{3}{5} + 8 =$	$24 + 4 \frac{3}{8} =$	$17 + 4 \frac{1}{2} =$

EXTRA!

Express the number of pencils in your desk as a fraction of all your writing utensils.

35

Fetching Sums

Write each sum in simplest form.

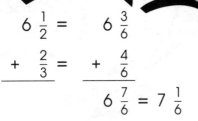

$6 \frac{1}{2} = \quad 6 \frac{3}{6}$

$+ \ \frac{2}{3} = \quad + \ \frac{4}{6}$

$6 \frac{7}{6} = 7 \frac{1}{6}$

Addition of mixed numbers and fractional numbers (like and unlike denominators)

$6 \frac{1}{12}$ $+ \ \frac{5}{12}$	$9 \frac{1}{6}$ $+ \ \frac{1}{6}$	$2 \frac{4}{7}$ $+ \ \frac{5}{7}$
$6 \frac{2}{3}$ $+ \ \frac{1}{3}$	$4 \frac{3}{4}$ $+ \ \frac{1}{4}$	$5 \frac{3}{8}$ $+ \ \frac{1}{8}$

$7 \frac{1}{5}$ $+ \ \frac{4}{5}$	$2 \frac{7}{10}$ $+ \ \frac{1}{10}$	$1 \frac{5}{8}$ $+ \ \frac{7}{8}$	$1 \frac{5}{16}$ $+ \ \frac{1}{16}$	$3 \frac{1}{4}$ $+ \ \frac{1}{4}$

$6 \frac{1}{2}$ $+ \ \frac{2}{3}$	$4 \frac{1}{2}$ $+ \ \frac{3}{5}$	$10 \frac{3}{8}$ $+ \ \frac{1}{2}$	$9 \frac{5}{12}$ $+ \ \frac{5}{6}$
$2 \frac{7}{9}$ $+ \ \frac{1}{3}$	$4 \frac{1}{5}$ $+ \ \frac{1}{10}$	$7 \frac{1}{5}$ $+ \ \frac{3}{10}$	$12 \frac{5}{6}$ $+ \ \frac{1}{2}$

Write a fraction that represents the number of brown-eyed students in your class.

Name _____ Date _____

Step by Step

A flight of stairs from easy to hard –
Can you reach the top
with no errors?

correct

28. $50\frac{1}{3}$
$+95\frac{5}{8}$

correct
_____

26. $47\frac{4}{9}$ 27. $6\frac{1}{2}$
$+32\frac{1}{6}$ $+8\frac{5}{12}$

correct
_____

23. $62\frac{1}{2}$ 24. $5\frac{2}{3}$ 25.
$40\frac{2}{3}$ $4\frac{5}{8}$ $20\frac{16}{20}$
$+89\frac{2}{5}$ $+3\frac{5}{6}$ $+89\frac{7}{10}$

correct
_____

19. $8\frac{4}{9}$ 20.   21.   22.
$6\frac{8}{9}$ $3\frac{4}{5}$ $6\frac{1}{3}$ $14\frac{1}{4}$
$+12\frac{2}{9}$ $+1\frac{1}{2}$ $+8\frac{5}{12}$ $+9\frac{7}{8}$

correct
_____

17. $18\frac{5}{8}$ 18. $9\frac{8}{10}$

14. $49\frac{3}{9}$ 15. $56\frac{4}{10}$ 16. $72\frac{6}{8}$ $10\frac{7}{8}$ $12\frac{7}{10}$
$+62\frac{8}{9}$ $+12\frac{9}{10}$ $+11\frac{5}{8}$ $+2\frac{4}{8}$ $+3\frac{4}{10}$

correct
_____

8. $2\frac{1}{8}$ 9. $3\frac{3}{9}$ 10. $4\frac{2}{5}$ 11. $8\frac{11}{12}$ 12. $4\frac{6}{8}$ 13. $24\frac{6}{10}$
$+6\frac{5}{8}$ $+2\frac{3}{9}$ $+3\frac{3}{5}$ $+10\frac{5}{12}$ $+18\frac{3}{8}$ $+14\frac{5}{10}$

correct
_____

1. $2\frac{1}{4}$ 2. $1\frac{1}{8}$ 3. $6\frac{1}{2}$ 4. $4\frac{3}{5}$ 5. $2\frac{2}{7}$ 6. $6\frac{1}{7}$ 7. $5\frac{2}{10}$
$+2\frac{1}{4}$ $+3\frac{2}{8}$ $+6\frac{1}{2}$ $+4\frac{1}{5}$ $+1\frac{1}{7}$ $+4\frac{1}{7}$ $+5\frac{3}{10}$

correct
_____

Number Mix-Up

Write each sum in its simplest form.

EXAMPLE:

$$35\tfrac{7}{8} = 35\tfrac{7}{8}$$
$$+36\tfrac{1}{2} = +36\tfrac{4}{8}$$
$$71\tfrac{11}{8} = 72\tfrac{3}{8}$$

$35\tfrac{7}{8}$ $+36\tfrac{1}{2}$	$13\tfrac{1}{6}$ $+\ 8\tfrac{1}{4}$

$25\tfrac{9}{10}$ $+\ 5\tfrac{3}{5}$	$4\tfrac{1}{3}$ $+24\tfrac{1}{6}$	$11\tfrac{1}{6}$ $+\ 9\tfrac{1}{2}$	$9\tfrac{1}{2}$ $+13\tfrac{1}{3}$
$68\tfrac{1}{2}$ $+25\tfrac{3}{8}$	$72\tfrac{3}{4}$ $+67\tfrac{5}{8}$	$7\tfrac{1}{3}$ $+19\tfrac{3}{4}$	$14\tfrac{2}{3}$ $+\ 7\tfrac{1}{2}$
$5\tfrac{4}{9}$ $+21\tfrac{2}{3}$	$74\tfrac{1}{4}$ $+43\tfrac{3}{8}$	$12\tfrac{7}{12}$ $+26\tfrac{3}{4}$	$50\tfrac{9}{10}$ $+17\tfrac{1}{2}$
$37\tfrac{5}{8}$ $+49\tfrac{1}{4}$	$9\tfrac{1}{3}$ $+17\tfrac{5}{8}$	$29\tfrac{5}{12}$ $+39\tfrac{1}{2}$	$45\tfrac{1}{2}$ $+27\tfrac{2}{5}$

Math Planet

Write each sum in its simplest form.

EXAMPLE:

$$8\frac{7}{10} = \quad 8\frac{7}{10}$$

$$+ 16\frac{1}{2} = + 16\frac{5}{10}$$

$$24\frac{12}{10} = 25\frac{2}{10} = 25\frac{1}{5}$$

$$8\frac{7}{10}$$
$$+ 16\frac{1}{2}$$

$3\frac{1}{4}$ $+ 18\frac{1}{2}$	$4\frac{1}{8}$ $+ 16\frac{1}{4}$	$3\frac{1}{8}$ $+ 16\frac{1}{2}$	$8\frac{1}{5}$ $+ 14\frac{1}{2}$
$7\frac{1}{3}$ $+ 17\frac{1}{4}$	$18\frac{1}{8}$ $+ \ 6\frac{9}{16}$	$71\frac{1}{16}$ $+ 56\frac{1}{2}$	$29\frac{3}{4}$ $+ 15\frac{1}{16}$
$52\frac{1}{2}$ $+ 63\frac{3}{4}$	$27\frac{3}{4}$ $+ 46\frac{1}{8}$	$60\frac{1}{2}$ $+ 69\frac{5}{16}$	$50\frac{2}{3}$ $+ 76\frac{1}{6}$
$91\frac{1}{2}$ $+ 52\frac{5}{8}$	$84\frac{5}{6}$ $+ 94\frac{2}{3}$	$78\frac{2}{3}$ $+ 27\frac{3}{4}$	$37\frac{2}{3}$ $+ 19\frac{1}{6}$

Dino Math

Find the sums and differences. Write each answer in simplest form.

1. $\dfrac{3}{5}$
   $+\dfrac{1}{5}$

2. $\dfrac{7}{8}$
   $-\dfrac{5}{8}$

3. $\dfrac{4}{9}$
   $+\dfrac{2}{9}$

4. $\dfrac{3}{4}$
   $+\dfrac{1}{4}$

5. $\dfrac{7}{12}$
   $-\dfrac{5}{12}$

6. $\dfrac{5}{6}$
   $-\dfrac{1}{6}$

7. $\dfrac{1}{10}$
   $+\dfrac{1}{2}$

8. $\dfrac{1}{6}$
   $+\dfrac{1}{3}$

9. $\dfrac{3}{4}$
   $-\dfrac{1}{2}$

10. $\dfrac{7}{10}$
    $-\dfrac{1}{5}$

11. $\dfrac{7}{8}$
    $+\dfrac{1}{4}$

12. $\dfrac{2}{3}$
    $-\dfrac{1}{6}$

13. $\dfrac{3}{4}$
    $+\dfrac{1}{2}$

14. $\dfrac{4}{9}$
    $-\dfrac{1}{3}$

15. $\dfrac{3}{10}$
    $+\dfrac{3}{5}$

Use a ruler to draw a line segment between each pair of fractions whose sum is 1.

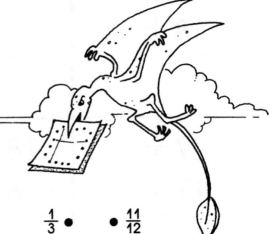

$\dfrac{1}{3}$ ●   ● $\dfrac{11}{12}$

$\dfrac{1}{5}$ ●   ● $\dfrac{5}{8}$

$\dfrac{3}{12}$ ●   ● $\dfrac{4}{8}$

$\dfrac{6}{10}$ ●   ● $\dfrac{3}{5}$

$\dfrac{1}{12}$ ●   ● $\dfrac{2}{3}$

$\dfrac{3}{8}$ ●   ● $\dfrac{8}{10}$

$\dfrac{1}{2}$ ●   ● $\dfrac{3}{4}$

$\dfrac{4}{10}$ ●   ● $\dfrac{2}{5}$

How many squares are drawn?

Fraction Fundamentals

Write in lowest terms.

1. $\frac{2}{6}$
    $+ \frac{3}{10}$

2. $\frac{3}{8}$
    $+ \frac{1}{2}$

3. $\frac{3}{10}$
    $+ \frac{1}{5}$

4. $\frac{2}{4}$
    $+ \frac{3}{5}$

5. $\frac{2}{3}$
    $+ \frac{4}{8}$

6. $\frac{7}{9}$
    $+ \frac{2}{18}$

7. $\frac{4}{6}$
    $+ \frac{3}{4}$

8. $\frac{2}{5}$
    $+ \frac{3}{6}$

9. $\frac{4}{8}$
    $+ \frac{1}{2}$

10. $\frac{4}{16}$
    $+ \frac{2}{8}$

Subtract. Remember to write in lowest terms.

1. $\frac{3}{5}$
    $- \frac{1}{2}$

2. $\frac{6}{8}$
    $- \frac{1}{2}$

3. $\frac{6}{10}$
    $- \frac{1}{5}$

4. $\frac{2}{3}$
    $- \frac{1}{2}$

5. $\frac{3}{8}$
    $- \frac{1}{10}$

6. $\frac{5}{6}$
    $- \frac{2}{3}$

7. $\frac{5}{12}$
    $- \frac{2}{8}$

8. $\frac{4}{5}$
    $- \frac{2}{4}$

9. $\frac{2}{3}$
    $- \frac{1}{8}$

10. $\frac{4}{8}$
    $- \frac{1}{6}$

11. $\frac{6}{7}$
    $- \frac{2}{14}$

12. $\frac{3}{9}$
    $- \frac{2}{18}$

13. $\frac{3}{4}$
    $- \frac{1}{5}$

14. $\frac{7}{10}$
    $- \frac{1}{2}$

15. $\frac{2}{3}$
    $- \frac{1}{4}$

EXTRA!

Write your age in months. Use fractions if necessary.

Missing: Math

Complete the exercises.

$$\frac{2}{3} - \frac{3}{8} = \frac{}{24} - \frac{}{24} = \frac{}{24}$$

$$\frac{5}{6} + \frac{1}{9} = \frac{}{18} + \frac{}{18} = \frac{}{18}$$

$$\frac{2}{3} + \frac{1}{4} = \frac{}{12} + \frac{}{12} = \frac{}{12} \qquad \frac{5}{6} - \frac{2}{9} = \frac{}{18} - \frac{}{18} = \frac{}{18}$$

$$\frac{3}{4} - \frac{2}{3} = \frac{}{12} - \frac{}{12} = \frac{}{12} \qquad \frac{2}{7} + \frac{1}{2} = \frac{}{14} + \frac{}{14} = \frac{}{14}$$

$$\frac{1}{8} + \frac{3}{4} = \frac{1}{8} + \frac{}{8} = \frac{}{8} \qquad \frac{1}{2} + \frac{1}{3} = \frac{}{6} + \frac{}{6} = \frac{}{6}$$

$$\frac{7}{9} - \frac{2}{3} = \frac{7}{9} - \frac{}{9} = \frac{}{9} \qquad \frac{2}{5} + \frac{1}{2} = \frac{}{10} + \frac{}{10} = \frac{}{10}$$

$$\frac{7}{10} - \frac{3}{5} = \frac{7}{10} - \frac{}{10} = \frac{}{10} \qquad \frac{1}{2} - \frac{2}{9} = \frac{}{18} - \frac{}{18} = \frac{}{18}$$

$$\frac{2}{3} - \frac{2}{15} = \frac{}{15} - \frac{2}{15} = \frac{}{15} \qquad \frac{4}{5} - \frac{1}{2} = \frac{}{10} - \frac{}{10} = \frac{}{10}$$

$$\frac{1}{2} + \frac{5}{12} = \frac{}{12} + \frac{5}{12} = \frac{}{12} \qquad \frac{5}{9} + \frac{1}{3} = \frac{5}{9} + \frac{}{9} = \frac{}{9}$$

$$\frac{3}{5} + \frac{1}{3} = \frac{}{15} + \frac{}{15} = \frac{}{15} \qquad \frac{1}{5} - \frac{1}{10} = \frac{}{10} - \frac{}{10} = \frac{}{10}$$

Choose one problem on this page and use words to explain how you solved it.

Fuel Up With Fractions

Write each sum or difference in its simplest form.

$\dfrac{7}{12}$ $+\dfrac{11}{12}$	$\dfrac{9}{11}$ $-\dfrac{3}{11}$	$\dfrac{11}{15}$ $-\dfrac{7}{15}$	$\dfrac{13}{15}$ $+\dfrac{7}{15}$

EXAMPLES:

$$\dfrac{3}{8} \quad = \quad \dfrac{3}{8}$$
$$+\dfrac{1}{4} \quad = \quad +\dfrac{2}{8}$$
$$\overline{\qquad\qquad\qquad \dfrac{5}{8}}$$

$\dfrac{13}{14}$ $-\dfrac{3}{14}$	$\dfrac{6}{7}$ $-\dfrac{2}{7}$	$\dfrac{1}{16}$ $+\dfrac{3}{16}$	$\dfrac{3}{20}$ $-\dfrac{1}{20}$

$$\dfrac{1}{2} \quad = \quad \dfrac{3}{6}$$
$$-\dfrac{1}{6} \quad = \quad -\dfrac{1}{6}$$
$$\overline{\qquad\qquad \dfrac{2}{6} = \dfrac{1}{3}}$$

$\dfrac{3}{8}$ $+\dfrac{1}{4}$	$\dfrac{1}{2}$ $-\dfrac{1}{6}$	$\dfrac{4}{9}$ $-\dfrac{1}{3}$	$\dfrac{3}{8}$ $+\dfrac{1}{4}$
$\dfrac{2}{3}$ $+\dfrac{1}{4}$	$\dfrac{7}{16}$ $-\dfrac{3}{8}$	$\dfrac{4}{5}$ $+\dfrac{2}{3}$	$\dfrac{3}{4}$ $-\dfrac{1}{2}$
$\dfrac{3}{4}$ $+\dfrac{2}{5}$	$\dfrac{9}{14}$ $-\dfrac{1}{7}$	$\dfrac{5}{8}$ $+\dfrac{1}{4}$	$\dfrac{5}{6}$ $+\dfrac{1}{12}$

The Magic Math Square

Add or subtract. Find the answer in the column on the right, and then write the number for the answer in the correct space in the box. You will form a "magic square." The sum of every row and column should be the same. The first one has been done for you.

A
$$3 \tfrac{2}{3}$$
$$+ \ 6 \tfrac{1}{3}$$

B
$$7 \tfrac{5}{6}$$
$$- \ 3 \tfrac{1}{6}$$

C
$$4 \tfrac{1}{2}$$
$$+ \ 3 \tfrac{1}{2}$$

D
$$5 \tfrac{3}{4}$$
$$- \ 1 \tfrac{1}{4}$$

E
$$8 \tfrac{8}{9}$$
$$- \ 3 \tfrac{5}{9}$$

F
$$2 \tfrac{3}{5}$$
$$+ \ 1 \tfrac{1}{5}$$

G
$$6 \tfrac{3}{8}$$
$$- \ 1 \tfrac{1}{8}$$

H
$$9 \tfrac{1}{2}$$
$$+ \ 2 \tfrac{1}{4}$$

I
$$10 \tfrac{1}{3}$$
$$- \ 4 \tfrac{1}{6}$$

J
$$12 \tfrac{3}{4}$$
$$+ \ 6 \tfrac{5}{8}$$

K
$$24 \tfrac{2}{3}$$
$$- \ 8 \tfrac{1}{5}$$

L
$$21 \tfrac{1}{2}$$
$$- \ 3 \tfrac{1}{8}$$

M
$$3 \tfrac{3}{7}$$
$$+ \ 4 \tfrac{1}{2}$$

N
$$8 \tfrac{2}{3}$$
$$+ \ 1 \tfrac{1}{2}$$

O
$$12 \tfrac{3}{5}$$
$$- \ 9$$

P
$$6 \tfrac{1}{2}$$
$$+ \ \tfrac{1}{5}$$

Answers

1. $6 \tfrac{7}{10}$
2. $4 \tfrac{2}{3}$
3. 8
4. $7 \tfrac{13}{14}$
5. $5 \tfrac{1}{3}$
6. $16 \tfrac{7}{15}$
7. $19 \tfrac{3}{8}$
8. $11 \tfrac{3}{4}$
9. $6 \tfrac{1}{6}$
10. $5 \tfrac{1}{4}$
11. $3 \tfrac{4}{5}$
12. $18 \tfrac{3}{8}$
13. $4 \tfrac{1}{2}$
14. $10 \tfrac{1}{6}$
15. $3 \tfrac{3}{5}$
16. 10

A 16	B	C	D
E	F	G	H
I	J	K	L
M	N	O	P

Sum _____

Simple Subtraction

Write each difference in simplest form.

$\frac{3}{4}$ = —— $-\frac{3}{8}$ = ——	$\frac{1}{3}$ = —— $-\frac{1}{7}$ = ——	$\frac{1}{2}$ = $\frac{5}{10}$ $-\frac{3}{10}$ = $\frac{3}{10}$ $\frac{2}{10}$ = $\frac{1}{5}$ Subtraction of fractional numbers (unlike denominators)
$\frac{2}{3}$ = —— $-\frac{2}{7}$ = ——	$\frac{5}{8}$ = —— $-\frac{1}{4}$ = ——	$\frac{5}{6}$ = —— $-\frac{5}{9}$ = ——	
$\frac{1}{2}$ = —— $-\frac{1}{9}$ = ——	$\frac{5}{6}$ = —— $-\frac{3}{5}$ = ——	$\frac{1}{2}$ = —— $-\frac{3}{10}$ = ——	$\frac{1}{3}$ = —— $-\frac{1}{8}$ = ——
$\frac{3}{5}$ = —— $-\frac{1}{3}$ = ——	$\frac{5}{6}$ = —— $-\frac{1}{2}$ = ——	$\frac{14}{15}$ = —— $-\frac{3}{5}$ = ——	$\frac{8}{9}$ = —— $-\frac{3}{4}$ = ——

List 3 real-life situations in which fraction are used.

Subtracting in Space

Solve these subtraction problems.

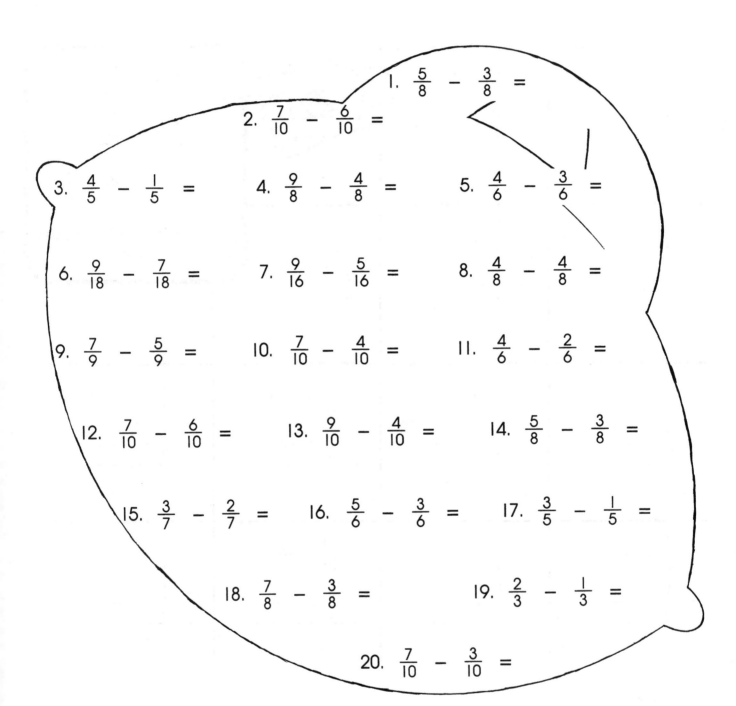

1. $\dfrac{5}{8} - \dfrac{3}{8} =$

2. $\dfrac{7}{10} - \dfrac{6}{10} =$

3. $\dfrac{4}{5} - \dfrac{1}{5} =$ 4. $\dfrac{9}{8} - \dfrac{4}{8} =$ 5. $\dfrac{4}{6} - \dfrac{3}{6} =$

6. $\dfrac{9}{18} - \dfrac{7}{18} =$ 7. $\dfrac{9}{16} - \dfrac{5}{16} =$ 8. $\dfrac{4}{8} - \dfrac{4}{8} =$

9. $\dfrac{7}{9} - \dfrac{5}{9} =$ 10. $\dfrac{7}{10} - \dfrac{4}{10} =$ 11. $\dfrac{4}{6} - \dfrac{2}{6} =$

12. $\dfrac{7}{10} - \dfrac{6}{10} =$ 13. $\dfrac{9}{10} - \dfrac{4}{10} =$ 14. $\dfrac{5}{8} - \dfrac{3}{8} =$

15. $\dfrac{3}{7} - \dfrac{2}{7} =$ 16. $\dfrac{5}{6} - \dfrac{3}{6} =$ 17. $\dfrac{3}{5} - \dfrac{1}{5} =$

18. $\dfrac{7}{8} - \dfrac{3}{8} =$ 19. $\dfrac{2}{3} - \dfrac{1}{3} =$

20. $\dfrac{7}{10} - \dfrac{3}{10} =$

46

Fractions Make All the Difference

Write each difference in simplest form.

$\frac{7}{8} - \frac{1}{8} =$			$\frac{4}{4} - \frac{1}{4} =$
$\frac{17}{10} - \frac{9}{10} =$	$\frac{11}{18} - \frac{5}{18} =$	$\frac{8}{9} - \frac{2}{9} =$	$\frac{19}{12} - \frac{9}{12} =$
$\frac{7}{9} - \frac{2}{9} =$	$\frac{7}{10} - \frac{4}{10} =$	$\frac{10}{13} - \frac{3}{13} =$	$\frac{13}{9} - \frac{7}{9} =$
$\frac{17}{12} - \frac{8}{12} =$	$\frac{7}{8} - \frac{3}{8} =$	$\frac{10}{9} - \frac{7}{9} =$	$\frac{19}{20} - \frac{11}{20} =$

$\frac{15}{10}$ $-\frac{9}{10}$	$\frac{17}{16}$ $-\frac{9}{16}$	$\frac{8}{9}$ $-\frac{5}{9}$	$\frac{11}{14}$ $-\frac{9}{14}$		
$\frac{7}{20}$ $-\frac{3}{20}$	$\frac{15}{12}$ $-\frac{7}{12}$	$\frac{11}{8}$ $-\frac{6}{8}$	$\frac{5}{6}$ $-\frac{2}{6}$	$\frac{19}{15}$ $-\frac{10}{15}$	$\frac{8}{7}$ $-\frac{4}{7}$
$\frac{6}{10}$ $-\frac{3}{10}$	$\frac{15}{18}$ $-\frac{11}{18}$	$\frac{12}{15}$ $-\frac{7}{15}$	$\frac{13}{10}$ $-\frac{7}{10}$	$\frac{7}{9}$ $-\frac{4}{9}$	$\frac{7}{12}$ $-\frac{6}{12}$

The Math Trainer

Write each difference in its simplest form.

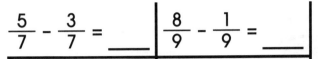

EXAMPLES:

$$\frac{5}{7} - \frac{3}{7} = \frac{2}{7}$$

$$5\frac{1}{9} = 4\frac{10}{9}$$
$$- \ 1\frac{7}{9} = - \ 1\frac{7}{9}$$
$$3\frac{3}{9} = 3\frac{1}{3}$$

$$\frac{5}{7} - \frac{3}{7} = \underline{\quad}$$

$$\frac{8}{9} - \frac{1}{9} = \underline{\quad}$$

$$\frac{9}{20} - \frac{3}{20} = \underline{\quad}$$

$$\frac{13}{18} - \frac{5}{18} = \underline{\quad}$$

$$\frac{8}{15} - \frac{1}{15} = \underline{\quad}$$

$$\frac{4}{9} - \frac{1}{9} = \underline{\quad}$$

$$\frac{9}{10} - \frac{3}{10} = \underline{\quad}$$

$$\frac{5}{21} - \frac{2}{21} = \underline{\quad}$$

$$\frac{9}{14} - \frac{5}{14} = \underline{\quad}$$

$$\frac{4}{15} - \frac{2}{15} = \underline{\quad}$$

$$\frac{11}{16} - \frac{5}{16} = \underline{\quad}$$

$$\frac{6}{7} - \frac{4}{7} = \underline{\quad}$$

$6\frac{4}{5}$ $- \ 2\frac{1}{5}$	$4\frac{1}{8}$ $- \ 2\frac{5}{8}$	$10\frac{2}{3}$ $- \ 3\frac{1}{3}$	$8\frac{13}{14}$ $- \ 8\frac{3}{14}$
$3\frac{1}{7}$ $- \ 1\frac{5}{7}$	$7\frac{3}{10}$ $- \ 5\frac{1}{10}$	$12\frac{7}{15}$ $- \ 4\frac{4}{15}$	$5\frac{7}{10}$ $- \ 2\frac{9}{10}$
$14\frac{3}{7}$ $-11\frac{1}{7}$	$23\frac{7}{8}$ $- \ 9\frac{5}{8}$	$15\frac{11}{12}$ $- \ 8\frac{7}{12}$	$11\frac{4}{9}$ $- \ 3\frac{5}{9}$

Subtraction Mix-Up

Write each difference in its simplest form.

EXAMPLE:

$$7\frac{1}{6} = 7\frac{1}{6} = 6\frac{7}{6}$$
$$-5\frac{1}{2} = -5\frac{3}{6} = -5\frac{3}{6}$$
$$1\frac{4}{6} = 1\frac{2}{3}$$

$7\frac{3}{8}$ $-\ 2\frac{1}{2}$	$5\frac{1}{5}$ $-\ 1\frac{1}{2}$	$4\frac{1}{8}$ $-\ 2\frac{1}{4}$	$6\frac{1}{3}$ $-\ 2\frac{3}{4}$
$6\frac{1}{5}$ $-\ 3\frac{3}{10}$	$5\frac{1}{4}$ $-\ 2\frac{1}{2}$	$4\frac{3}{10}$ $-\ 1\frac{4}{5}$	$8\frac{1}{3}$ $-\ 2\frac{5}{6}$
$7\frac{1}{3}$ $-\ 4\frac{8}{15}$	$8\frac{1}{5}$ $-\ 6\frac{7}{10}$	$9\frac{3}{4}$ $-\ 4\frac{11}{12}$	$7\frac{1}{6}$ $-\ 5\frac{1}{2}$
$6\frac{4}{9}$ $-\ 3\frac{2}{3}$	$3\frac{3}{8}$ $-\ 1\frac{1}{2}$	$9\frac{1}{7}$ $-\ 6\frac{3}{14}$	$4\frac{1}{8}$ $-\ 3\frac{3}{4}$

Math Bugs

Write each difference in simplest form.

$10\frac{2}{3}$ $-\ \frac{1}{3}$	$8\frac{1}{4}$ $-\ \frac{1}{4}$

$$6\frac{1}{3} = \qquad 6\frac{2}{6} = \qquad 5\frac{8}{6}$$
$$-\ \frac{1}{2} = \qquad -\ \frac{3}{6} = \qquad -\ \frac{3}{6}$$
$$\qquad\qquad\qquad\qquad\qquad 5\frac{5}{6}$$

$9\frac{4}{9}$ $-\ \frac{2}{9}$	$7\frac{3}{7}$ $-\ \frac{2}{7}$	$3\frac{3}{8}$ $-\ \frac{1}{4}$

$4\frac{2}{5}$ $-\ \frac{1}{5}$	$5\frac{3}{8}$ $-\ \frac{1}{8}$	$5\frac{3}{4}$ $-\ \frac{3}{8}$	$4\frac{4}{5}$ $-\ \frac{1}{10}$	$6\frac{1}{3}$ $-\ \frac{1}{6}$

$9\frac{1}{3}$ $-\ \frac{5}{6}$	$6\frac{1}{4}$ $-\ \frac{1}{2}$	$7\frac{1}{4}$ $-\ \frac{2}{3}$

$7\frac{1}{4}$ $-\ \frac{3}{4}$	$10\frac{1}{7}$ $-\ \frac{3}{7}$	$4\frac{3}{8}$ $-\ \frac{3}{4}$

$3\frac{1}{10}$ $-\ \frac{1}{2}$	$8\frac{1}{3}$ $-\ \frac{2}{3}$	$2\frac{1}{10}$ $-\ \frac{1}{5}$

Name _____   Date _____

Mixed Differences

Write each difference in its simplest form.

$10\frac{1}{3}$ $-\ 8\frac{11}{15}$	$8\frac{1}{6}$ $-\ 5\frac{1}{3}$	$9\frac{1}{12}$ $-\ 3\frac{3}{4}$	$4\frac{1}{5}$ $-\ 2\frac{3}{10}$
$11\frac{2}{5}$ $-\ 7\frac{7}{10}$	$12\frac{4}{9}$ $-\ 4\frac{2}{3}$	$4\frac{1}{6}$ $-\ 3\frac{2}{3}$	$6\frac{1}{12}$ $-\ 4\frac{5}{6}$
$9\frac{1}{4}$ $-\ 5\frac{1}{3}$	$8\frac{1}{2}$ $-\ 3\frac{7}{8}$	$5\frac{1}{2}$ $-\ 2\frac{5}{6}$	$6\frac{3}{10}$ $-\ 1\frac{1}{2}$
$16\frac{1}{4}$ $-\ 9\frac{3}{4}$	$8\frac{3}{10}$ $-\ 4\frac{7}{10}$	$7\frac{5}{12}$ $-\ 2\frac{7}{12}$	$5\frac{1}{7}$ $-\ 2\frac{1}{2}$

EXTRA!

Write five of your answers in order from least to greatest.

Fraction Subtraction

Write each difference in its simplest form.

EXAMPLE:

$$1\frac{1}{6} = \frac{7}{6}$$
$$-\ \frac{5}{6} = -\ \frac{5}{6}$$
$$\frac{2}{6} = \frac{1}{3}$$

$$38\frac{5}{7}$$
$$-\ \frac{3}{7}$$

$$1\frac{1}{6}$$
$$-\ \frac{5}{6}$$

$$3\frac{3}{8}$$
$$-\ \frac{5}{8}$$

$$4\frac{1}{4}$$
$$-\ \frac{3}{4}$$

$$8\frac{1}{10}$$
$$-\ \frac{1}{2}$$

$$5\frac{2}{5}$$
$$-\ \frac{9}{10}$$

$$7\frac{1}{6}$$
$$-\ \frac{2}{3}$$

$$2\frac{2}{9}$$
$$-\ \frac{1}{3}$$

$$7\frac{3}{4}$$
$$-\ \frac{1}{2}$$

$$8\frac{9}{10}$$
$$-\ \frac{2}{5}$$

$$4\frac{2}{3}$$
$$-\ \frac{1}{6}$$

$$4\frac{1}{5}$$
$$-\ \frac{3}{10}$$

$$12\frac{1}{10}$$
$$-\ \frac{4}{5}$$

$$3\frac{2}{7}$$
$$-\ \frac{1}{2}$$

$$6\frac{1}{6}$$
$$-\ \frac{1}{3}$$

Math Mixer

Write each difference in its simplest form.

EXAMPLE:

$$24\frac{2}{15} = 23\frac{17}{15}$$
$$- \quad 6\frac{11}{15} = - \quad 6\frac{11}{15}$$
$$\overline{\qquad} \qquad \overline{17\frac{6}{15} = 17\frac{2}{5}}$$

$$10\frac{1}{5}$$
$$- \quad 6\frac{3}{5}$$

$$5\frac{3}{7}$$
$$- \quad 1\frac{6}{7}$$

$$11\frac{5}{12}$$
$$- \quad 3\frac{11}{12}$$

$$6\frac{3}{7}$$
$$- \quad 4\frac{5}{7}$$

$$9\frac{2}{5}$$
$$- \quad 5\frac{3}{5}$$

$$8\frac{3}{10}$$
$$- \quad 2\frac{9}{10}$$

$$21\frac{2}{15}$$
$$- \quad 8\frac{7}{15}$$

$$12\frac{1}{12}$$
$$- \quad 5\frac{7}{12}$$

$$7\frac{1}{10}$$
$$- \quad 6\frac{3}{10}$$

$$15\frac{3}{8}$$
$$- 11\frac{7}{8}$$

$$30\frac{1}{8}$$
$$- 17\frac{7}{8}$$

$$25\frac{4}{9}$$
$$- \quad 6\frac{7}{9}$$

$$24\frac{3}{14}$$
$$- 23\frac{11}{14}$$

$$18\frac{2}{7}$$
$$- 13\frac{6}{7}$$

Fun with Fractions

Write each difference in its simplest form.

$$20$$
$$-\ 5\frac{3}{4}$$
_____

$$50\frac{5}{6}$$
$$-\ \frac{1}{6}$$
_____

$$3\frac{7}{8}$$
$$-\ \frac{3}{4}$$
_____

EXAMPLE:

$$20 \quad = \quad 19\frac{4}{4}$$
$$-\ 5\frac{3}{4} \quad = \quad -\ 5\frac{3}{4}$$
_____
$$14\frac{1}{4}$$

EXAMPLE:

$$9\frac{1}{5} = 9\frac{3}{15} = 8\frac{18}{15}$$
$$-\ \frac{2}{3} = -\ \frac{10}{15} = -\ \frac{10}{15}$$
_____
$$8\frac{8}{15}$$

$$5\frac{4}{5}$$
$$-\ \frac{1}{2}$$
_____

$$57$$
$$-\ 18\frac{2}{3}$$
_____

$$5\frac{3}{4}$$
$$-\ \frac{4}{5}$$
_____

$$2\frac{1}{3}$$
$$-\ \frac{2}{3}$$
_____

$$15$$
$$-\ 6\frac{2}{5}$$
_____

$$9\frac{1}{5}$$
$$-\ \frac{2}{3}$$
_____

$$4\frac{1}{3}$$
$$-\ \frac{1}{2}$$
_____

$$99$$
$$-\ 88\frac{3}{8}$$
_____

$$4\frac{1}{2}$$
$$-\ \frac{5}{6}$$
_____

$$2\frac{5}{12}$$
$$-\ \frac{3}{4}$$
_____

$$9\frac{1}{3}$$
$$-\ \frac{5}{6}$$
_____

Name_____ Date _____

Simplifying Subtraction

Subtract and simplify these fractions.

82 $-\ \ \frac{6}{8}$	$10\frac{3}{6}$ $-\ 2\frac{4}{6}$	$11\frac{2}{10}$ $-\ 3\frac{4}{10}$	$14\frac{2}{7}$ $-\ 7\frac{6}{7}$
$62\frac{5}{12}$ $-40\frac{7}{12}$	$14\frac{2}{7}$ $-\ 6\frac{6}{7}$	$5\frac{3}{10}$ $-\ 2\frac{7}{10}$	$9\frac{3}{8}$ $-\ 4\frac{7}{8}$
$10\frac{1}{5}$ $-\ 5\frac{3}{5}$	$6\frac{1}{8}$ $-\ 3\frac{4}{8}$	$18\frac{2}{16}$ $-17\frac{5}{16}$	$22\frac{2}{14}$ $-20\frac{3}{14}$
$85\frac{1}{6}$ $-\ 1\frac{9}{6}$	$2\frac{8}{10}$ $-\ 1\frac{9}{10}$	$6\frac{1}{5}$ $-\ 2\frac{4}{5}$	$4\frac{1}{8}$ $-\ 2\frac{3}{8}$
$6\frac{1}{9}$ $-\ 2\frac{6}{9}$	18 $-\ \ \frac{2}{8}$	$4\frac{5}{10}$ $-\ 2\frac{9}{10}$	6 $-\ 3\frac{5}{7}$
$34\frac{7}{10}$ $-30\frac{9}{10}$	$20\frac{8}{12}$ $-10\frac{9}{12}$	$5\frac{1}{10}$ $-\ 1\frac{3}{10}$	$39\frac{3}{8}$ $-29\frac{5}{8}$

Discovering Differences

Write each difference.

$15\frac{5}{6}$ $-\ 8$	$9\frac{4}{9}$ $-\ 6$	$12\frac{3}{4}$ $-\ 7$
$4\frac{1}{3}$ $-\ 2$	$8\frac{3}{5}$ $-\ 5$	$10\frac{1}{2}$ $-\ 4$

$$\begin{array}{ccc} 12\frac{3}{4} & 20 & =\ 19\frac{9}{9} \\ -\ 7 & -11\frac{4}{9} & =\ -11\frac{4}{9} \\ \hline 5\frac{3}{4} & & 8\frac{5}{9} \end{array}$$

29 $-18\frac{1}{10}$	15 $-\ 6\frac{7}{10}$	20 $-11\frac{4}{9}$	22 $-\ 6\frac{2}{9}$
7 $-\ 3\frac{1}{3}$	21 $-10\frac{2}{3}$	11 $-\ 9\frac{1}{8}$	9 $-\ 4\frac{5}{8}$
24 $-20\frac{1}{12}$	18 $-\ 3\frac{3}{4}$	17 $-\ 7\frac{1}{7}$	6 $-\ 2\frac{2}{5}$

EXTRA! Use a book or other resource to investigate the history of the Radio Flyer® wagon. Write a paragraph about your findings.

Making More Fractions

Write each product in its simplest form.

EXAMPLE:

$$\frac{\overset{1}{\cancel{2}}}{\underset{1}{\cancel{3}}} \times \frac{\overset{1}{\cancel{3}}}{\underset{4}{\cancel{8}}} = \frac{1}{4}$$

$\frac{7}{10} \times \frac{5}{6} =$ ___	$\frac{5}{8} \times \frac{1}{4} =$ ___	$\frac{2}{3} \times \frac{1}{9} =$ ___	
$\frac{1}{3} \times \frac{9}{10} =$ ___	$\frac{1}{4} \times \frac{8}{11} =$ ___	$\frac{8}{15} \times \frac{5}{6} =$ ___	$\frac{3}{10} \times \frac{2}{3} =$ ___
$\frac{6}{7} \times \frac{5}{6} =$ ___	$\frac{3}{14} \times \frac{7}{12} =$ ___	$\frac{7}{9} \times \frac{3}{7} =$ ___	$\frac{4}{11} \times \frac{3}{16} =$ ___
$\frac{2}{5} \times \frac{5}{9} =$ ___	$\frac{7}{11} \times \frac{3}{14} =$ ___	$\frac{1}{12} \times \frac{4}{5} =$ ___	$\frac{3}{4} \times \frac{4}{7} =$ ___
$\frac{1}{12} \times \frac{2}{5} =$ ___	$\frac{4}{5} \times \frac{15}{16} =$ ___	$\frac{9}{16} \times \frac{2}{3} =$ ___	$\frac{3}{5} \times \frac{5}{12} =$ ___
$\frac{3}{20} \times \frac{4}{9} =$ ___	$\frac{8}{9} \times \frac{5}{12} =$ ___	$\frac{3}{4} \times \frac{8}{15} =$ ___	$\frac{2}{5} \times \frac{7}{12} =$ ___
$\frac{9}{10} \times \frac{5}{18} =$ ___	$\frac{3}{20} \times \frac{5}{9} =$ ___	$\frac{2}{5} \times \frac{5}{8} =$ ___	$\frac{5}{8} \times \frac{4}{15} =$ ___

$\frac{2}{9} \times \frac{3}{5} \times \frac{5}{8} =$ ___	$\frac{4}{5} \times \frac{5}{6} \times \frac{1}{2} =$ ___	$\frac{3}{7} \times \frac{1}{3} \times \frac{7}{10} =$ ___

Create a fraction multiplication problem that uses 25 and 20 as the denominators. Solve it and have a friend check your answer.

Multiplication Mania

Write each product as a whole number or mixed number in simplest form.

$\frac{3}{5} \times 35 = \frac{3}{5} \times \frac{\overset{7}{\cancel{35}}}{1} = \frac{3 \times 7}{1 \times 1} = 21$

$\frac{1}{2} \times 72 =$

$\frac{1}{9} \times 27 =$

$\frac{1}{9} \times 72 =$

$\frac{1}{6} \times 30 =$

$\frac{1}{4} \times 16 =$

$\frac{1}{3} \times 9 =$

$\frac{1}{2} \times 12 =$

$12 \times \frac{1}{12} =$

$77 \times \frac{1}{7} =$

$22 \times \frac{1}{11} =$

$75 \times \frac{1}{3} =$

$88 \times \frac{1}{11} =$

$118 \times \frac{1}{2} =$

$24 \times \frac{5}{12} =$

$15 \times \frac{5}{9} =$

$\frac{1}{2} \times 17 =$

$\frac{3}{11} \times 11 =$

$\frac{1}{3} \times 20 =$

$60 \times \frac{2}{5} =$

$15 \times \frac{5}{6} =$

$\frac{3}{5} \times 35 =$

$\frac{3}{4} \times 12 =$

$\frac{2}{9} \times 27 =$

Write the page number you would be looking at if you were $\frac{1}{3}$ into your math textbook.

Multiplication Wheels

Multiply. Write the products as mixed numbers or whole numbers in the blank spaces on the wheel.

Missing: Math

Follow the arrows. Divide to complete the triangle.

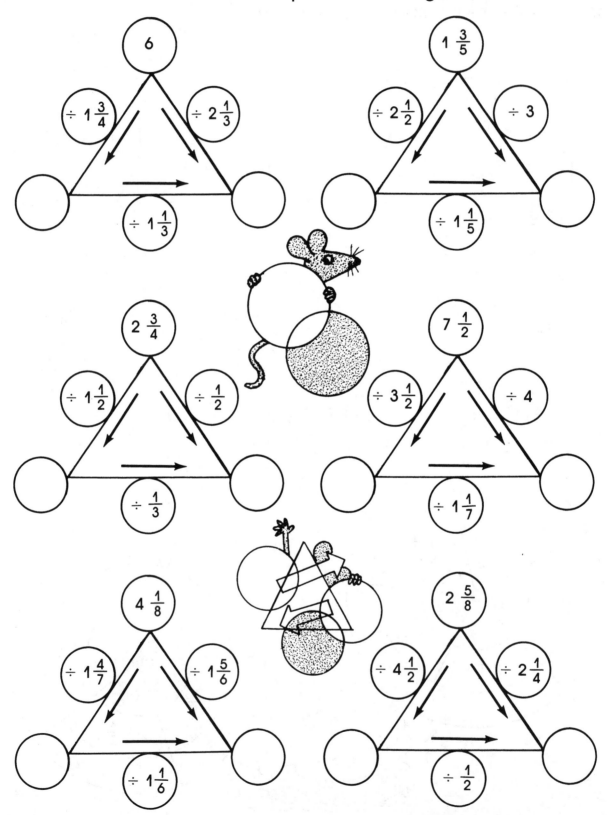

Math Conversions

Write each division problem as multiplication problem
and name the product.

$$12 \div \frac{1}{2} = \frac{12}{1} \times \frac{2}{1} = 24$$

$$\frac{1}{2} \div 3 = \frac{1}{2} \times \frac{1}{3} = \frac{1}{6}$$

$\frac{1}{8} \div 5 = \frac{1}{8} \times$

$\frac{1}{12} \div 4 = \frac{1}{12} \times$

$\frac{1}{2} \div 2 =$

$\frac{1}{8} \div 6 =$

$\frac{1}{3} \div 8 =$

$\frac{1}{4} \div 7 = \frac{1}{4} \times$

$\frac{1}{5} \div 2 = \frac{1}{5} \times$

$\frac{1}{7} \div 6 = \frac{1}{7} \times$

$\frac{1}{6} \div 3 = \frac{1}{6} \times$

$\frac{1}{10} \div 3 =$

$\frac{1}{9} \div 3 =$

$\frac{1}{5} \div 5 =$

$9 \div \frac{1}{8} = 9 \times$

$7 \div \frac{1}{3} = 7 \times$

$2 \div \frac{1}{4} = 2 \times$

$4 \div \frac{1}{2} = 4 \times$

$11 \div \frac{1}{10} = 11 \times$

$20 \div \frac{1}{6} = 20 \times$

$15 \div \frac{1}{3} =$

$21 \div \frac{1}{4} =$

$29 \div \frac{1}{2} =$

Use two answers from this paper to create a multiplication problem. Solve it and
have a friend check your answer.

Fraction Puzzler

Across:

2. $\frac{9}{11} + \frac{12}{11} = \frac{x}{11}$

4. $13\frac{3}{3} = x$

7. $\frac{11}{2} + \frac{13}{2}$

9. $\frac{1}{x} = \frac{5}{100}$

10. $\frac{17}{3} - \frac{4}{3} = \frac{x}{3}$

11. $\frac{100}{4} = x$

12. $25 - 12\frac{6}{6}$

14. $\frac{186}{6} = x$

15. $80\frac{7}{7} = x$

17. $\frac{34}{2} = x$

18. $2,064\frac{1}{2} + 2,065\frac{1}{2}$

21. $4,820\frac{3}{4} - 2,208\frac{3}{4}$

24. $22 + 17\frac{7}{7}$

25. $8\frac{3}{5} + 9\frac{2}{5}$

26. $\frac{5}{75} = \frac{1}{x}$

28. $\frac{51}{2} + \frac{31}{2}$

29. $\frac{94}{3} - \frac{16}{3}$

31. $100 - 79\frac{5}{5}$

32. $1 = \frac{x}{16}$

34. $\frac{17}{20} - \frac{4}{20} = \frac{x}{20}$

35. $\frac{1}{12} = \frac{x}{144}$

36. $54\frac{8}{8} = x$

Down:

1. $\frac{6}{66} = \frac{1}{x}$

2. $20\frac{1}{2} + 200\frac{1}{2}$

3. $\frac{21}{4} + \frac{19}{4}$

4. $22 - 10\frac{5}{5}$

5. $420 + 17\frac{2}{2}$

6. $\frac{3}{45} = \frac{1}{x}$

8. $\frac{84}{2} - \frac{42}{2}$

11. $26\frac{8}{8} = x$

13. $40\frac{8}{9} - 16\frac{8}{9}$

14. $\frac{1}{3} = \frac{10}{x}$

16. $\frac{x}{24} = \frac{1}{2}$

17. $\frac{1}{4} = \frac{3}{x}$

19. $\frac{2}{x} = \frac{1}{7}$

20. $\frac{903}{3} = x$

22. $612\frac{1}{4} - 1\frac{1}{4}$

23. $\frac{29}{3} + \frac{25}{3}$

27. $51\frac{5}{5} = x$

28. $\frac{4}{5} = \frac{x}{50}$

30. $200\frac{1}{5} + 410\frac{4}{5}$

31. $366 - 130\frac{5}{5}$

33. $61\frac{10}{10} = x$

34. $\frac{x}{15} = 1$

Cosmic Math Crossword

Across:

3. $\frac{2}{6} + \frac{1}{12} = \frac{5}{x}$

5. $\frac{1}{5} + \frac{1}{3} = \frac{8}{x}$

7. $12 - \frac{7}{7}$

9. $\frac{1}{10} + \frac{1}{20} = \frac{3}{x}$

10. $50 - (\frac{1}{2} - \frac{2}{4})$

11. $(\frac{5}{5} + \frac{6}{6}) + 310$

13. $\frac{2}{3} - \frac{1}{4} = \frac{5}{x}$

14. $\frac{1}{2} + \frac{1}{5} = \frac{7}{x}$

15. $\frac{2}{7} + \frac{1}{2} = \frac{11}{x}$

16. $\frac{2}{3} - \frac{1}{5} = \frac{7}{x}$

17. $\frac{1}{7} + \frac{1}{2} = \frac{9}{x}$

19. $103\frac{2}{2} - \frac{4}{4}$

21. $216 - \frac{10}{10}$

23. $98\frac{3}{3} + \frac{4}{4}$

24. $17 - \frac{10}{5}$

25. $\frac{1}{15} + \frac{1}{5} = \frac{4}{x}$

27. $(\frac{3}{3} + \frac{4}{4}) + 18$

28. $\frac{2}{3} - \frac{1}{7} = \frac{11}{x}$

29. $101 - \frac{10}{x} = 100$

30. $9 + (\frac{4}{4} + \frac{2}{2})$

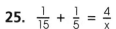
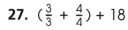

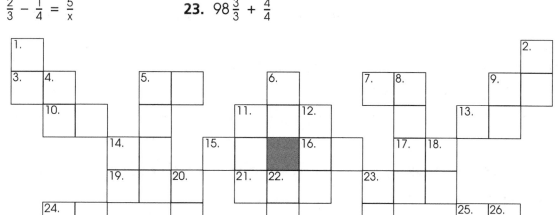

Down:

1. $13 - (\frac{2}{2} + \frac{3}{3})$

2. $\frac{1}{5} + \frac{1}{10} = \frac{3}{x}$

4. $25 - (\frac{2}{6} - \frac{1}{3})$

5. $1{,}001 - \frac{6}{6}$

6. $\frac{2}{3} + \frac{1}{4} = \frac{x}{12}$

8. $1{,}009 + \frac{5}{5}$

9. $\frac{3}{11} + \frac{1}{2} = \frac{17}{x}$

11. $(\frac{6}{6} - \frac{4}{4}) + 342$

12. $216 - \frac{9}{9}$

14. $\frac{1}{2} + \frac{2}{7} = \frac{x}{14}$

18. $44 - \frac{16}{4}$

20. $300 + \frac{4}{2}$

22. $\frac{1}{2} - \frac{1}{10} = \frac{4}{x} = \frac{2}{5}$

23. $102 - \frac{6}{3}$

24. $(\frac{6}{6} + \frac{2}{2}) + 8$

26. $49 + \frac{4}{2}$

27. $\frac{1}{10} - \frac{1}{20} = \frac{1}{x}$

31. $\frac{1}{4} + \frac{3}{16} = \frac{7}{x}$

School of Fractions

Work the problems below. Show your answers in simplest form.

1. On a history test Susan answered $\frac{7}{10}$ of the questions correctly. What fraction of the questions did she miss? _____

2. The fifth grade presented a program for their parents. $\frac{2}{9}$ of the students played in the band, $\frac{2}{9}$ sang in the chorus, and $\frac{4}{9}$ had parts in the play. What part of the students took part in the program? _____

3. John cut a cake into 12 equal pieces. He ate $\frac{2}{12}$, Damon ate $\frac{2}{12}$, and Chandra ate $\frac{1}{12}$. What part of the cake was eaten? _____

4. Four–sevenths of the students in Ms. Perry's class are girls. What part of the students are boys? _____

5. Two–thirds of the students at Central School walk to school. The others ride the bus. What part of the students ride the bus? _____

6. Five–eighths of the students in Dan's class bought lunch on Monday. $\frac{7}{8}$ bought lunch on Tuesday. How many more bought lunch on Tuesday? _____

7. $\frac{3}{5}$ of the cars on the parking lot are four–door cars. The rest are two–door cars. What part are two–door cars? _____

8. $\frac{1}{6}$ of the bikes in the bike rack are blue. $\frac{2}{6}$ of the bikes are green. What part are either blue or green? _____

9. In the library $\frac{1}{4}$ of the students chose science–fiction stories, $\frac{1}{4}$ chose biographies, and $\frac{1}{4}$ chose adventure stories. The other students did not find books they liked. What part of the students did not choose a book? _____

10. $\frac{1}{4}$ of the students in Ms. Bailin's class completed their math lessons during study period. The rest of the students read their library books during study period. What part of the students read library books? _____

11. Carl was assigned 10 division problems in math class. He solved $\frac{3}{10}$ of them during class and $\frac{4}{10}$ of them during study period. What part does he have left to complete at home? _____

Take a survey to find what fraction of the students in your class brought their lunch from home today. What fraction will order from the cafeteria?

A Part of a Whole

1. Annie and Lyndi each needed $50.00 to go to a basketball camp. Annie had $\frac{3}{5}$ of the money she needed. Lyndi had $\frac{7}{10}$ of the money she needed. How much money did each girl have? Annie _____ Lyndi _____

2. During the morning Erin completed $\frac{3}{8}$ of her math problems. In the afternoon she completed another $\frac{1}{2}$ of the problems. How much of the math assignment did Erin have completed when she left school?_____

3. Aimee worked $15\frac{5}{6}$ minutes on the exercise bike on Monday and $12\frac{2}{3}$ minutes on Wednesday. How much total time did Aimee work out on the exercise bike on those two days?_____

4. Justin swam for $2\frac{1}{4}$ hours on Saturday and $3\frac{1}{3}$ hours on Sunday. How much longer did he swim on Sunday than on Saturday? _____ How much time did Justin spend swimming this weekend?_____

5. Tom has to ride his bicycle $2\frac{1}{7}$ miles to school each day. How many miles will Tom ride each day to and from school? _____ How many miles will he ride in a week?_____

6. Judd has a big problem. He needs to simplify the following fractions, but he isn't sure what to do. Simplify these fractions for Judd.

$$\frac{9}{12} = \qquad \frac{14}{18} = \qquad \frac{12}{20} = \qquad \frac{10}{12} = \qquad \frac{8}{24} =$$

7. Keith needed $5\frac{1}{2}$ pounds of nails for a shed he was rebuilding. The hardware store had only $3\frac{7}{8}$ pounds of nails. How many pounds of nails was Keith short?

_____

8. Mrs. McJenkins' class was making a stew. Angela bought $3\frac{1}{2}$ lbs. of meat, Kevin brought $1\frac{1}{4}$ lbs. of carrots, Heather brought $\frac{3}{8}$ lbs. of celery, and Lindsay brought $6\frac{1}{2}$ lbs. of potatoes. How many pounds of ingredients did the students bring?_____

What fraction of states in the United States has at least one border touching the Atlantic Ocean?

Recording Math

On an old VCR tape, the counter will begin at 0 and advance to 600. Slow speed will record for 6 hours. Standard speed will record for 4 hours. Fast speed will record for 2 hours.

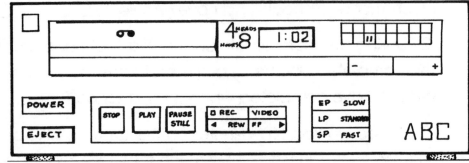

1. Two hours of taping at slow speed will use what fractional part of the tape? _____ standard speed? _____ fast speed? _____

2. Approximately what reading will show on the counter when $\frac{1}{3}$ of the tape has been used? _____

$\frac{1}{2}$ has been used? _____ $\frac{1}{6}$ has been used? _____

$\frac{5}{6}$ has been used? _____ $\frac{2}{3}$ has been used? _____

3. Four events, using equal time, are recorded on the tape. Each event used what part of the tape? _____ Two events will use what part? _____ Three events? _____

4. Refer to question 3. Approximately what counter reading will show at the beginning of the second event? _____ The third event? _____ The fourth event? _____

5. One-tenth of each hour on the tape records a commercial. How much of the total tape is used for commercials with 2 hours of recording? _____ 3 hours of recording? _____ 4 hours of recording? _____ 6 hours of recording? _____

6. You started to watch a 3-hour movie on the VCR at 8 p.m. Bedtime is at 10 p.m. What fractional part of the movie did you see? _____ Not see? _____

7. You plan to tape the Winter Olympics for two hours (slow speed) each night for a week (seven days). How many tapes will you need? _____ What fractional part of the last tape will be left? _____

Find the length of your favorite movie or television show. Express this time in hours. Use fractions if necessary.

Meet the Junior Super Stars

1. In the first race of the season, there were 15 runners. $\frac{1}{3}$ finished the race in less than 2 minutes. How many runners did this? _____

2. There were 124 participants in the track meet.
Half of them were boys. How many were girls? _____

3. Maria finished her race in $3\frac{1}{4}$ minutes. Scott finished in $4\frac{1}{4}$ minutes. José finished in $2\frac{1}{4}$ minutes. How many total minutes to run all three races? _____

4. Tony was in every race. His total running times were $32\frac{1}{2}$ minutes. The team total was 84 minutes. How many minutes remain if Tony's are removed? _____

5. In Minh's three high jump tries he scored $4\frac{1}{2}$ feet, $4\frac{1}{8}$ feet, and $3\frac{3}{8}$ feet. How many total feet did he jump? _____

6. Manuel threw the discus three times. His scores were: 60 feet, 68 feet, and 70 feet. What was his total distance? _____

7. Georgia got refreshments for some of the 124 team members. She bought soda for $\frac{1}{4}$ of them. How many sodas did she buy? _____ If each soda cost 50¢, what was the total cost? _____
What was her change from a $20 bill? _____

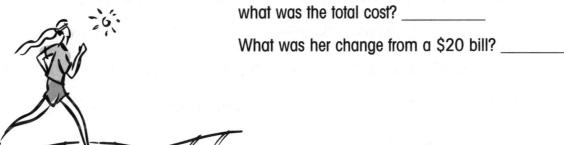

What physical activities must you complete if you participate in a triathlon?

Solving Story Problems

1. Janet spends $\frac{2}{3}$ of her allowance on school lunches and $\frac{1}{6}$ on entertainment.  What part of her allowance is left? _____

2. Shantel earned $2.50 babysitting. She spent $\frac{3}{5}$ of it on a book. How much did she pay for the book? _____

3. Bill received his $5.00 allowance on Friday. On Saturday he spent $2.00. What fraction of his allowance did he spend? _____

4. Tom spent $\frac{3}{4}$ of his $6.00 allowance on comic books. How much did he spend? _____

5. Anne, Gina, and Mary shared the cost of a $3.60 box of candy. If each girl paid the same amount, how much did each pay? _____

6. Ed spent $\frac{3}{5}$ of his $4.00 allowance. Carlos spent $\frac{3}{4}$ of his $3.00 allowance. Who spent the most? _____ How much more? _____

7. Nita saved $\frac{3}{8}$ of her $6.00 birthday gift. How much did she save? _____

8. Peggy borrowed $\frac{1}{6}$ of the cost of a $9.00 watch from her mother. How much did she borrow? _____

9. Alex earned $270.00 at his summer job. He spent $\frac{1}{3}$ on a bicycle, $\frac{2}{9}$ on a tape player, and $\frac{1}{6}$ on a fiberglass bow. How much did the bicycle cost? _____

10. Jasmine earns $140.00 each week. How much does she spend if $\frac{1}{4}$ of her money is deducted for taxes? _____; $\frac{1}{2}$ is spent on entertainment? _____; $\frac{1}{5}$ is spent on clothing? _____; and $\frac{1}{20}$ is put into savings? _____

 Imagine you earned an allowance of $10 per week. Express your use of this $10 using fractions.

A Problem of Fractions

Complete the problems.

1. $\frac{3}{5}$ of the flowers in a garden were red. Tawana picked $\frac{1}{2}$ of the red flowers. What part of the flowers in the garden did Tawana pick? _____ of the flowers

2. $\frac{2}{3}$ of the fish in a bowl were goldfish. $\frac{1}{5}$ of the goldfish were placed in another bowl. What part of all the fish were placed in another bowl? _____ of all the fish

3. A recipe calls for $\frac{2}{3}$ cup of milk. How much milk is needed for $\frac{1}{2}$ of the recipe? _____ cup

4. $\frac{4}{7}$ of the children in a class wore jeans. $\frac{1}{3}$ of the children wearing jeans left to help in the lunchroom. What part of the class went to help in the lunchroom? _____ of the class

5. $\frac{1}{5}$ of the children in a class wear glasses. $\frac{1}{2}$ of the children who wear glasses have black hair. What part of the class have black hair and wear glasses? _____

6. A package of bacon weighs $\frac{3}{4}$ of a pound. $\frac{1}{2}$ of the package has been used. What part of a pound of bacon has been used? _____ pound

7. Lisa has $\frac{3}{4}$ yards of ribbon. She made a bow from $\frac{1}{3}$ of it. What part of a yard did Lisa use to make a bow? _____ yards

8. $\frac{1}{8}$ of the fifth grade children practiced for a math contest. $\frac{1}{3}$ of those who practiced were chosen for the math team. What part of the fifth grade children were chosen for the team? _____ of the children

9. $\frac{1}{4}$ of the books in a library are non-fiction. $\frac{1}{8}$ of the non-fiction books are biographies. What part of the books in the library are biographies? _____ of the books

10. $\frac{5}{6}$ of the children in a school ate lunch at school. $\frac{2}{3}$ of those who ate lunch at school bought milk. What part of the children in the school bought milk? _____ of the children

Math Riddle

Write each fraction or decimal as a percent. Then use the answers to solve the riddle at the bottom of the page.

0.25 = _____ D	$\frac{1}{5}$ = _____ I	$\frac{9}{25}$ = _____ L
0.75 = _____ S	0.37 = _____ O	$\frac{1}{2}$ = _____ T
$\frac{1}{10}$ = _____ E	0.19 = _____ N	0.60 = _____ E

0.30 = _____ A	$\frac{3}{20}$ = _____ R
$\frac{4}{5}$ = _____ E	.48 = _____ L

What is the difference between a new twenty dollar bill and an old one?

$\overline{}$ $\overline{}$ $\overline{}$ $\overline{}$ $\overline{}$ $\overline{}$ $\overline{}$ $\overline{}$
19%   20%   19%   10%   50%   60%   80%   19%

$\overline{}$ $\overline{}$ $\overline{}$ $\overline{}$ $\overline{}$ $\overline{}$ $\overline{}$
25%   37%   36%   48%   30%   15%   75%

Whose face is on the twenty dollar bill?

Multiplying Parts

Multiply these decimal fractions.

A.
$$\begin{array}{r} 1.2 \\ \times\ .3 \\ \hline \end{array}$$
$$\begin{array}{r} 6.8 \\ \times\ .2 \\ \hline \end{array}$$
$$\begin{array}{r} 24.1 \\ \times\ .05 \\ \hline \end{array}$$
$$\begin{array}{r} 6.05 \\ \times\ .02 \\ \hline \end{array}$$
$$\begin{array}{r} 16.1 \\ \times\ .4 \\ \hline \end{array}$$

B.
$$\begin{array}{r} 10.8 \\ \times\ .4 \\ \hline \end{array}$$
$$\begin{array}{r} 15.6 \\ \times\ .35 \\ \hline \end{array}$$
$$\begin{array}{r} 20.2 \\ \times\ .6 \\ \hline \end{array}$$
$$\begin{array}{r} 85.9 \\ \times\ .52 \\ \hline \end{array}$$
$$\begin{array}{r} 46.9 \\ \times\ .08 \\ \hline \end{array}$$

Multiply. Express as a decimal.

C.
$$\frac{2}{10} \times \frac{3}{100}$$
$$\frac{8}{10} \times \frac{4}{10}$$
$$\frac{16}{100} \times \frac{6}{10}$$
$$\frac{5}{100} \times \frac{6}{100}$$
$$\frac{3}{10} \times \frac{3}{10}$$

D.
$$\frac{9}{10} \times \frac{2}{10}$$
$$\frac{20}{100} \times \frac{2}{100}$$
$$\frac{1}{10} \times \frac{40}{100}$$
$$\frac{14}{100} \times \frac{20}{100}$$
$$\frac{2}{10} \times \frac{5}{10}$$

E.
$$\frac{4}{100} \times \frac{8}{100}$$
$$\frac{42}{100} \times \frac{2}{10}$$
$$\frac{6}{100} \times \frac{4}{10}$$
$$\frac{20}{1000} \times \frac{2}{1000}$$
$$\frac{4}{10} \times \frac{6}{100}$$

Pair Them Up!

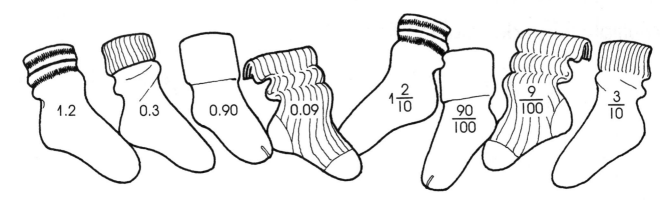

Write as decimals.

A. $\frac{8}{10}$ = $\frac{4}{100}$ =

B. $\frac{8}{100}$ = $\frac{4}{10}$ =

C. $\frac{80}{100}$ = $\frac{40}{100}$ =

Write as fractions.

D. 0.60 =   0.3 =

E. 0.06 =   0.30 =

F. 0.6 =   0.03 =

Write as decimals.

G. $\frac{45}{100}$ = $\frac{11}{100}$ = $7\frac{30}{100}$ = $12\frac{10}{100}$ =

H. $\frac{60}{100}$ = $\frac{15}{100}$ = $5\frac{60}{100}$ = $28\frac{40}{100}$ =

I. $\frac{5}{100}$ = $\frac{13}{100}$ = $1\frac{40}{100}$ = $3\frac{4}{100}$ =

J. $\frac{29}{100}$ = $\frac{20}{100}$ = $8\frac{4}{100}$ = $9\frac{3}{100}$ =

K. $\frac{13}{100}$ = $\frac{1}{100}$ = $6\frac{5}{100}$ = $9\frac{30}{100}$ =

Write as fractions or mixed numbers in simplest form.

L. .2	.75	.9	.05
M. .25	.3	.12	.35
N. 6.25	2.5	6.2	3.25
O. .37	.62	7.7	4.12
P. .28	5.75	.45	3.6

Name_____ Date _____

A Puzzle of Parts

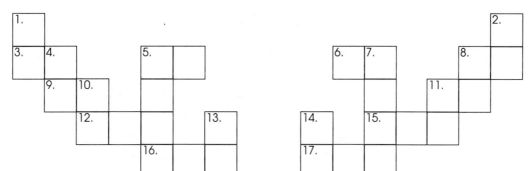

Across:

3. $70 + \frac{2}{2}$

5. $1.2 + 2.3 + 1.7$

6. $3\frac{1}{4} = \frac{x}{4}$

8. $\frac{1}{3} + \frac{1}{7} = \frac{10}{x}$

9. $0.9 - 0.14$

11. $\frac{1}{3} - \frac{1}{5} = \frac{2}{x}$

12. $1.03 + 1.04 + 1.05$

15. $213 - (\frac{1}{2} + \frac{1}{2})$

16. $10.15 - 6.09$

17. $105 + \frac{4}{4}$

18. $6.12 + 7.11 + 8.12$

21. $\frac{144}{12} = x$

22. $\frac{12}{56} = \frac{3}{x}$

23. $3\frac{1}{5} + 7\frac{4}{5}$

24. $\frac{63}{6} = \frac{x}{2}$

26. $1.3 + 1.5 + 0.6$

27. $3\frac{1}{8} = \frac{x}{8}$

28. $\frac{100}{10} = x$

29. $23.09 - 8.81$

32. $675.91 + 675.91$

Down:

1. $0.6 - 0.13$

2. $\frac{5}{13} + \frac{6}{13} = \frac{x}{13}$

4. $2 - 0.3$

5. $3.54 + 1.684$

7. $\frac{4}{2} + 3024$

8. $3\frac{4}{7} = \frac{x}{7}$

10. $\frac{189}{3} = x$

11. $\frac{5}{12} + \frac{1}{2} = \frac{11}{x}$

13. $1.151 - 0.789$

14. $214 + (\frac{3}{4} + \frac{1}{4})$

19. $\frac{23}{2} = x\frac{1}{2}$

20. $0.1846 + 0.1408$

22. $300.61 - 169.19$

25. $8.327 + 4.108$

27. $250.672 - 49.327$

29. $6\frac{1}{2} = \frac{x}{2}$

30. $0.07 + 0.07 + 0.07$

31. $2.4 + 3.5 + 2.9$

32. $\frac{1}{9} - \frac{1}{18} = \frac{1}{x}$

33. $\frac{125}{5} = x$

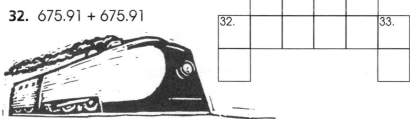

Place Value Puzzler

932.62537

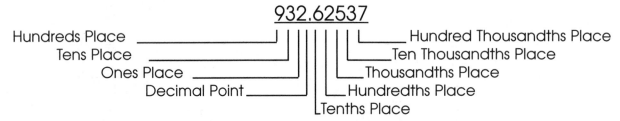

Hundreds Place _____

Tens Place _____

Ones Place _____

Decimal Point _____

Tenths Place

Hundredths Place

Thousandths Place

Ten Thousandths Place

Hundred Thousandths Place

The above number is read as follows: Nine hundred thirty-two and sixty-two thousand five hundred thirty-seven hundred thousandths. The word **and** indicates the decimal point.

EXAMPLES:

A. Twenty-one and eight tenths   21.8
B. Seven and one hundred thirteen thousandths   7.113
C. Fifty-one and three hundredths   51.03
D. Six and two thousand one hundred two ten thousandths   6.2102

Across:

2. Twenty-one and sixty-two hundredths
6. Five thousand two hundred sixteen ten thousandths
9. Six and three tenths
11. One thousand two hundred ten and fourteen thousandths
14. Sixty-seven hundredths
15. Two hundred fifty-six and nine hundred ten thousandths
17. Three hundred thirty-one thousandths
18. Seventy-two and one thousand two hundred ten ten thousandths
20. Thirty-three hundredths
21. Forty-three and six hundred forty-two thousandths
22. Six hundred one and seven hundredths
23. Six and one tenth
24. Twenty-nine and seven tenths
25. Sixty-four thousandths

Down:

1. Four hundred sixty-two and thirty-two hundredths
3. Ten and ninety-four hundredths
4. Two hundred ten and six tenths
5. Two hundred three thousandths
6. Five thousand four hundred seventy-one ten thousandths
7. Eighteen and seventeen hundredths
8. Two hundred seventy and fourteen hundredths
10. Three thousand five hundred thirty-nine ten thousandths
12. One and thirty-two hundredths
13. Sixteen thousandths
14. Six thousand one hundred sixty-six ten thousandths
16. Thirteen and five tenths
19. Two and six hundredths

Name_____ Date _____

Place Value Puzzler 2

932.62537

Hundreds Place _____
Tens Place _____
Ones Place _____
Decimal Point _____
Tenths Place
Hundred Thousandths Place
Ten Thousandths Place
Thousandths Place
Hundredths Place

The above number is read as follows: Nine hundred thirty–two **and** sixty–two thousand five hundred thirty–seven hundred thousandths. The word **and** indicates the decimal point.

EXAMPLES:

A. Fifty–six and four hundred twelve thousandths 56.412
B. Seven hundred four and sixty–two ten thousandths 704.0062
C. Four and ten thousand sixteen hundred thousandths 4.10016
D. Three hundred eighteen and nine hundredths 318.09

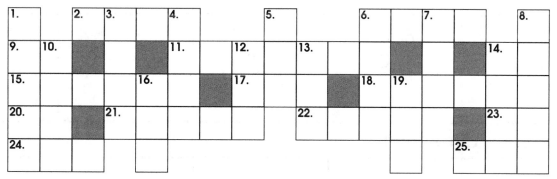

Across:

2. Fifty–six and twenty–three hundredths
6. Two thousand eight hundred twenty–six ten thousandths
9. One and two tenths
11. Twenty–one and ten thousand two hundred fifty–seven hundred thousandths
14. Five and six tenths
15. Ten and two thousand one hundred ten ten thousandths
17. Four and twenty–six hundredths
18. One hundred twenty and one hundred thousandths
20. Two hundredths
21. Sixteen and two hundred two thousandths
22. Thirty thousand two hundred one hundred thousandths
23. Seven hundredths
24. Fifty–two and seven tenths
25. Sixty–three thousandths

Down:

1. Two hundred eleven and five hundredths
3. Six and four hundred eleven thousandths
4. Three hundred twenty and two tenths
5. Ninety and two tenths
6. Two thousand seven hundred twelve ten thousandths
7. Two and seven hundred one thousandths
8. Four and six thousand seventy–three ten thousandths
10. Two thousand twenty–two ten thousandths
12. One hundred forty–two thousandths
13. Twenty–six and three tenths
14. Fifty and six, hundredths
16. Sixteen and eight tenths
19. Twenty and four tenths

Sheriff Sum & Subtract

Write each sum.

5.3 + 4.0	0.5 + 0.2	9.1 + 2.8	
0.1 + 0.7	4.5 + 3.1	0.3 + 0.6	0.31 + 0.89
0.25 + 0.13	6.67 + 1.02	9.25 + 1.34	13.54 + 21.07	50.6 + 9.05

Write each difference.

0.3 − 0.1	9.0 − 2.5	0.5 − 0.4	7.6 − 4.8	0.4 − 0.1
5.9 − 2.0	3.4 − 0.4	0.7 − 0.3	0.84 − 0.06	0.29 − 0.18
8.42 − 5.71	1.68 − 1.23	0.61 − 0.59	9.53 − 6.37	0.57 − 0.36

EXTRA! What's the difference between the price of a school lunch and the price of a gallon of milk?

Discovering Decimals

Write each sum or difference.

$$
\begin{array}{r} {\scriptstyle 1\ 1} \\ 15.6 \\ +\ 7.6 \\ \hline 23.2 \end{array}
\qquad
\begin{array}{r} {\scriptstyle 9\ \ 9} \\ 2\,\overset{1}{0}.\overset{1}{0}\,\overset{1}{0} \\ -15.99 \\ \hline 4.01 \end{array}
$$

Addition and subtraction of decimal fractions

		$\begin{array}{r}7.10\\-\ 2.03\\\hline\end{array}$	$\begin{array}{r}6.83\\+\ 5.9\\\hline\end{array}$	$\begin{array}{r}7.28\\+\ 4.91\\\hline\end{array}$
		$\begin{array}{r}15.6\\+\ 7.6\\\hline\end{array}$	$\begin{array}{r}38.32\\-34.86\\\hline\end{array}$	$\begin{array}{r}66.80\\-\ 7.03\\\hline\end{array}$
$\begin{array}{r}35.46\\+\ 6.8\\\hline\end{array}$	$\begin{array}{r}19.95\\+\ 0.39\\\hline\end{array}$	$\begin{array}{r}17.02\\-15.6\\\hline\end{array}$	$\begin{array}{r}26.22\\+15.99\\\hline\end{array}$	$\begin{array}{r}30.73\\+15.90\\\hline\end{array}$
$\begin{array}{r}22.45\\+\ 0.95\\\hline\end{array}$	$\begin{array}{r}19.83\\+\ 0.6\\\hline\end{array}$	$\begin{array}{r}0.98\\-\ 0.79\\\hline\end{array}$	$\begin{array}{r}2.08\\+\ 3.07\\\hline\end{array}$	$\begin{array}{r}19.35\\+\ 6.07\\\hline\end{array}$
$\begin{array}{r}18.04\\-10.9\\\hline\end{array}$	$\begin{array}{r}20.10\\+18.95\\\hline\end{array}$	$\begin{array}{r}3.69\\-\ 0.98\\\hline\end{array}$	$\begin{array}{r}40.02\\-\ 7.9\\\hline\end{array}$	$\begin{array}{r}51.50\\+13.75\\\hline\end{array}$
$\begin{array}{r}36.32\\-35.91\\\hline\end{array}$	$\begin{array}{r}33.77\\+\ 0.68\\\hline\end{array}$	$\begin{array}{r}5.10\\-\ 2.83\\\hline\end{array}$	$\begin{array}{r}13.52\\-12.86\\\hline\end{array}$	$\begin{array}{r}52.90\\+15.99\\\hline\end{array}$
$\begin{array}{r}15.7\\-\ 6.38\\\hline\end{array}$	$\begin{array}{r}6.2\\+\ 7.35\\\hline\end{array}$	$\begin{array}{r}10.50\\+\ 3.07\\\hline\end{array}$	$\begin{array}{r}16.8\\+15.8\\\hline\end{array}$	$\begin{array}{r}29.70\\-\ 4.21\\\hline\end{array}$
$\begin{array}{r}60.5\\+\ 8.02\\\hline\end{array}$	$\begin{array}{r}9.28\\+\ 6.95\\\hline\end{array}$	$\begin{array}{r}20.00\\-15.99\\\hline\end{array}$	$\begin{array}{r}48.00\\-15.23\\\hline\end{array}$	$\begin{array}{r}25.00\\-13.08\\\hline\end{array}$

Watch That Point!

Divide by 10? Move one place to the left.
Divide by 100? Move two places to the left.
Divide by 1000? _____
Divide by 10,000? _____

Got the point? Try these.

A. $47.5 \div 10 =$ $6.5 \div 10 =$ $23.91 \div 1000 =$

B. $47.5 \div 100 =$ $.39 \div 10 =$ $7.44 \div 100 =$

C. $47.5 \div 1000 =$ $8.53 \div 100 =$ $5.32 \div 1000 =$

D. $47.5 \div 10,000 =$ $.97 \div 1000 =$ $.014 \div 100 =$

To multiply, move right.
Multiply by 10? Move one place to the right.
Multiply by 100? Move two places to the right.
Multiply by 1000? _____
Multiply.

E. $47.5 \times 10 =$ $2.65 \times 100 =$ $4.56 \times 1000 =$

F. $47.5 \times 100 =$ $54.93 \times 1000 =$ $3.449 \times 10 =$

G. $47.5 \times 1000 =$ $7.612 \times 10 =$ $.9763 \times 100 =$

H. $47.5 \times 10,000 =$ $35.7 \times 100 =$ $.931 \times 10,000 =$

Watch the signs!

I. $5.8 \times 100 =$ $71.0 \div 100 =$ $5.32 \times 10 =$

J. $22.4 \div 100 =$ $1.026 \times 1000 =$ $.43 \div 100 =$

Name something that is commonly grouped by the hundreds.

Smooth Sailing

Dividing decimals by a whole number? Remember to place the quotient decimal directly above the divided decimal.

Write each quotient.

A. $4\overline{)1.16}$ $6\overline{)54.6}$ $3\overline{)1.2}$ $4\overline{)1.6}$ $9\overline{)87.3}$

B. $7\overline{)9.8}$ $2\overline{)1.06}$ $5\overline{)52.0}$ $8\overline{)5.68}$ $6\overline{)18.78}$

C. $34\overline{)8.84}$ $16\overline{)9.6}$ $21\overline{)7.728}$ $38\overline{)7.6}$ $32\overline{).768}$

D. $13\overline{)3.926}$ $27\overline{)9.72}$ $63\overline{)50.4}$ $36\overline{)8.64}$ $15\overline{)61.5}$

E. $82\overline{)33.292}$ $16\overline{)5.232}$ $43\overline{)34.486}$ $15\overline{)3.750}$ $36\overline{)84.24}$

Find the average yearly rainfall for your state. How much rain does your state see in a month?

Detective Division

Divide. Then solve the riddle.

$4\overline{)12.20}$	$5\overline{)32.5}$	$3\overline{)0.168}$	$9\overline{)9.063}$	$.12\overline{)1.44}$	$3.7\overline{)296}$
M	T	R	F	S	E

$21\overline{)123.9}$	$.02\overline{)27.68}$	$2.9\overline{)10.44}$	$8.4\overline{)68.04}$	$.08\overline{).248}$
O	E	L	V	I

$6\overline{)15.9}$	$5.3\overline{)4.452}$	$.03\overline{)1.116}$	$17\overline{)57.8}$	$4.1\overline{)8.569}$	$.07\overline{)2.45}$
R	E	T	H	T	E

How do you make 7 even?
Write the letters on the correct blanks.

.056	80	3.05	5.9	8.1	.84

6.5	3.4	35

1.007	3.1	.056	12	37.2

3.6	1384	2.09	6.5	80	2.65

Name_____ Date _____

Keep the Change

Write each difference.

$78.27 − 40.28	$91.74 − 72.15	$75.93 − 73.26	$90.41 − 65.10	$62.92 − 46.18
$78.66 − 62.78	$43.65 − 30.68	$99.65 − 85.88	$65.53 − 2.18	$95.70 − 34.33
$48.10 − 31.78	$93.23 − 3.15	$62.21 − 3.58	$90.03 − 84.21	$91.41 − 76.05
$29.35 − 27.16	$83.02 − 58.35	$84.14 − 40.02	$ 9.70 − 4.24	$97.99 − 88.63
$ 5.32 − 1.78	$ 7.18 − 4.33	$52.63 − 13.86	$64.43 − 5.11	$98.34 − 28.46

Use the internet or a newspaper to find the price of a gallon of milk. Find the cost of your favorite kind of cereal. Add the prices together. What is your total?

It's in the Ballpark

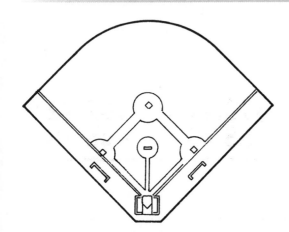

Ballpark figures can be used to estimate prices when you are shopping.

$$\begin{array}{rcr} \$45.10 & = & \$45 \\ + 16.80 & = & 17 \\ \hline \$61.90 & & \$62 \end{array}$$

If the digit to the right of the decimal is 5 or greater, round the whole number up. If it is less than 5, round down.

The estimate of $62 is close enough. Round to the nearest dollar and estimate the sums. Then check the problems by adding the exact amounts and comparing your answers with your estimates.

A.
$$\begin{array}{rcl} \$18.60 & = & 19 \\ + 28.30 & = & \underline{28} \end{array}$$
$$\begin{array}{rcl} \$34.70 & = & \\ + 7.20 & = & \underline{} \end{array}$$
$$\begin{array}{rcl} \$9.10 & = & \\ + 8.89 & = & \underline{} \end{array}$$
$$\begin{array}{rcl} \$24.70 & = & \\ + 8.30 & = & \underline{} \end{array}$$

B.
$$\begin{array}{rcl} \$28.23 & = & \\ .43 & = & \\ 3.93 & = & \\ + 4.57 & = & \underline{} \end{array}$$
$$\begin{array}{rcl} \$47.19 & = & \\ 1.72 & = & \\ 6.35 & = & \\ + 3.95 & = & \underline{} \end{array}$$
$$\begin{array}{rcl} \$214.72 & = & \\ 972.16 & = & \\ .84 & = & \\ + 7.49 & = & \underline{} \end{array}$$
$$\begin{array}{rcl} \$18.97 & = & \\ 7.60 & = & \\ 9.80 & = & \\ + 5.82 & = & \underline{} \end{array}$$

Round and estimate the differences. Check your estimate with the actual product.

C.
$$\begin{array}{rcl} \$72.36 & = & \\ - 9.26 & = & \underline{} \end{array}$$
$$\begin{array}{rcl} \$58.21 & = & \\ - 5.94 & = & \underline{} \end{array}$$
$$\begin{array}{rcl} \$24.62 & = & \\ - 7.23 & = & \underline{} \end{array}$$
$$\begin{array}{rcl} \$36.52 & = & \\ - 7.44 & = & \underline{} \end{array}$$

Estimate to answer this question: Will $5 be enough to purchase one pair of socks at $2.75, shoestrings at $1.69, and a comb at $.79? Explain your answer.

Puppetry!

To make a puppet, the following materials are needed:

$\frac{3}{4}$ yd. fur fabric	$3.79 per yard
$\frac{1}{8}$ yd. felt	$1.25 per yard
glue-on eyes	15¢ for 2
thread	85¢
glue	$1.95

1. Jenny wanted to make four puppets. How much fur fabric was needed?
   _____

2. What was the cost?_____

3. How much felt was needed? _____ Cost? _____
   (Round up)

4. How many eyes? _____ Cost?_____

5. What is the cost so far? _____ For one puppet?_____

6. Jenny needed thread and glue. That made the total cost _____.

7. Sara wanted six puppets. The store had 4 yards of fur left. Was that enough?
   _____

8. Could she make five puppets?_____

9. How much fur would be left over?_____

10. If they work together, how much felt do the girls need?_____

Write the name of a famous puppet. Use an encyclopedia or the internet to help you.

Banking

deposit	withdraw	increase	decrease	balance	interest

1. Mr. LaMarche deposited $81.62 and wrote a check for $26.95. What was the total change in his bank balance? _____

2. Ms. Allen deposited 2 twenty–dollar bills, 1 five–dollar bill, 3 one–dollar bills, 3 quarters, and 6 nickels. How much did she deposit? _____

3. Jeffrey had a balance of $56.17 in his savings account. He deposited $6.58. What is his new balance? _____

4. Anita received $25.00 for her birthday. She spent $18.25 for a new sweater and put the rest of the money in her savings account. How much did she put in her account? _____

5. Tom had $37.25 in his savings account. The bank paid him 4% interest on his account. Find his new balance. _____

6. Mr. Garcia deposited $53.25 in cash and checks of $19.47, $34.22, and $14.55. What was his total deposit? _____

7. Susan put 8 one–dollar bills, 3 quarters, 5 dimes, and 4 nickels in her savings account. How much did she add to her savings account? _____

8. Charlotte had a balance of $61.07 in her savings account. She withdrew $14.50. What is her new balance? _____

9. George had $52.70 in his checking account. He spent 10% of his money. How much did he have left in his checking account? _____

10. Gavin borrowed $650 from the bank. They charged him 9% interest for one year. How much interest must he pay? _____

Use the internet or an encyclopedia to find out how banks were started. Write a few sentences about the history of banks.

Garage Sale

1. George was the cashier at the Ericson family garage sale. He went to the bank to get change
   for his cash box.

   a) How many quarters could he get for $10? _____

   b) 40 nickels is the same as _____ dollars.

   c) How many dimes could he get for $5? _____

2. At the bank George changed $20.00 into smaller bills and coins. He got 20 quarters, 20 dimes,
   20 nickels, and the balance in one–dollar bills. How many $1.00 bills did he receive? _____

3. Janet bought a game for 50¢, 2 books at 25¢ each, and a coffee mug for 15¢. How much
   change should she receive from $2? _____

4. Mrs. King bought 5 glasses for 10¢ each, a baking pan for 35¢, and a vase for 65¢. How much
   did she spend? _____

5. Martin bought a baseball cap for 85¢. What amount of change did he receive from $1.00? ____

6. Andy bought 4 cereal bowls for 60¢. What was the cost of each bowl? _____

7. Helena bought a stuffed toy for 75¢, a necklace for 15¢, and a game for 35¢.
   How much did she spend? _____

8. Robert bought a bundle of magazines for $1.35. There were 15 magazines in the bundle.
   How much did he pay for each magazine? _____

9. At the end of the day George took the money from his cash box. He had 8 five–dollar bills,
   42 one–dollar bills, 6 half–dollars, 65 quarters, 28 nickels, 19 dimes, and 25 pennies.
   How much money did he have? _____

10. George had put $20.00 in change into the cash box before the sale began.
    How much did the Ericsons make at their sale? _____

11. The Ericsons' sale was successful because they advertised. They spent $2.65 on a newspaper ad,
    90¢ for poster paper, and 87¢ for markers. How much did they spend on advertising? _____

EXTRA!

Make a list of five items you would sell if you had a garage sale. How much would
you charge for each item? How much would you make if you sold all of your items?

Missing: Math

Make each sentence true. Write =, <, or > between the numerals.

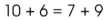

10 + 6	7 + 8		
3 x 10	2 x 15		

10 + 6 = 7 + 9
10 plus 6 is equal to 7 plus 9.

10 + 6 < 7 + 10
10 plus 6 is less than 7 plus 10.

10 + 6 > 7 + 8
10 plus 6 is greater than 7 plus 8.

Comparing numbers

18 ÷ 3	12 ÷ 2	17 − 4	20 − 5	84 ÷ 7	78 ÷ 6
9 x 7	8 x 8	15 + 4	3 + 7	11 − 7	13 − 9
(2 x 3) + 5	(4 x 2) + 1	7 x 8	6 x 9	2 + (3 x 4)	8 + (3 x 3)
36 + 8	26 + 18	90 ÷ 9	45 ÷ 5	52 − 14	75 − 37
69 ÷ 3	92 ÷ 4	6 + (9 − 2)	10 + (8 − 5)	5 + (8 ÷ 2)	4 + (27 ÷ 9)
16 x 3	12 x 4	33 − 9	41 − 18	96 ÷ 8	75 ÷ 5

Which is greater, the difference between your age and your mom's age or the difference between your mom's and grandmother's ages?

Math Maze

Write <, >, or = to make each statement true.

1) 6.7 ___ 6.8

2) 40.3 ___ 40.29

3) .50 ___ .5

4) .742 ___ .75

5) .620 ___ .619

6) .1502 ___ .1512

7) .001 ___ .0010

8) .04 ___ .040

9) .038 ___ .308

10) 12.09 ___ 12.090

11) .4 ___ .04

12) 9.6 ___ 8.6

13) 25.2 ___ 25.02

14) 36.1 ___ 36.10

15) 5.19 ___ 5.20

16) .36 ___ .360

17) 2.2 ___ 2.199

18) 5.05 ___ 5.55

19) 2.5 ___ 2.49

20) 1.001 ___ 1.0010

21) 46.908 ___ 46.809

22) .6660 ___ .666

23) 1.1021 ___ 1.1021

24) 16.168 ___ 16.1680

25) 95.7 ___ 95.69

26) 31.126 ___ 31.216

27) 10.05 ___ 10.50

28) 6.097 ___ 6.0970

29) 15.90 ___ 15.9

30) 17.07 ___ 17.070

31) 49.63 ___ 49.36

32) .009 ___ .0090

33) .387 ___ .3875

34) .10 ___ .100

35) 24.07 ___ 24.17

36) 8.340 ___ 8.34

Connect the answers to find your way through the maze.

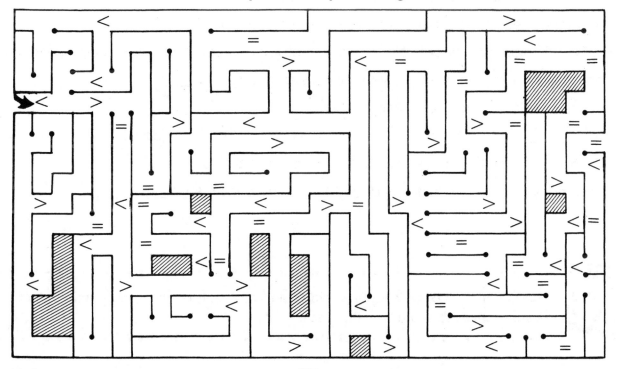

Name_____ Date _____

Time to Figure

60 seconds (sec.) = 1 minute (min.)	52 weeks (wk.) = 1 year (yr.)
60 minutes (min.) = 1 hour (hr.)	12 months (mo.) = 1 year (yr.)
24 hours (hr.) = 1 day (d.)	365 days (d.) = 1 year (yr.)
7 days (d.) = 1 week (wk.)	100 years (yr.) = 1 century

1. Robert skipped rope for 120 seconds, ran for 240 seconds, and walked for 120 seconds. How many minutes did he exercise? _____

2. Dolores attends math class 5 days a week for 45 minutes each day. How many hours and minutes does she spend in class in one week? _____

3. America celebrated its bicentennial (200th) birthday in 1976. How many centuries is this? _____

4. A Japanese woman was born in 1863 and died in 1975. How many years did she live? Was this more than a century? _____

5. Some people can hold their breath underwater for 3 minutes. How many seconds is this? _____

6. The first artificial satellite, *Sputnik I*, remained in orbit for 92 days. How many weeks and days was it in orbit? _____

7. The crew of Apollo XVII was on the moon for about 75 hours. How many "earth" days and hours were they on the moon? _____

8. In 1995, Russian cosmonaut Valery Polyakov returned to Earth after remaining in orbit for 439 days. Give the length of time in years, weeks, and days. _____

9. On your tenth birthday how old are you in:

   a) _____ months? b) _____ weeks? c) _____ days?

10. On a winter day the sun rose at 6:47 a.m. and set at 5:42 p.m. How many hours and minutes of daylight were there that day? _____

Use the internet or an encyclopedia to find more information on Sputnik I. Write a few sentences to share with the class.

Timely Problems

1. Jacob and Ryan are scheduled to leave on a flight at 2:25 p.m. It is now 11:50 a.m. How long will it be until their plane leaves?_____

2. Lisa ran 3 miles. Each mile was timed at 5 minutes 40 seconds. How long did Lisa run?_____

3. Tiffany gets up at 7:10 a.m. each school day. It takes her 1 hour and 15 minutes to shower, dress, eat, and walk to school. What time does she get to school?_____

4. Mrs. Beckett's flight arrived at 1:15 p.m. The flight had lasted 2 hours and 40 minutes. What time did her flight leave?_____

5. For the students at Downing Elementary School, classes begin at 8:35 a.m. The school day lasts 6 hours and 45 minutes. What time does school dismiss each day?_____

6. Keith ran a marathon in 3 hours and 27 minutes. The race began at 7:45 a.m. What time did Keith finish? _____ The winner finished 43 minutes earlier. What time did the winner finish?_____

7. Mr. Lee wanted to call a business partner in Japan. It was 9:00 a.m. in New York. The time in Japan is 14 hours later than in New York. What time is it in Japan?_____

8. Jeremy decided to go sailing. He began his adventure at 1:15 p.m. on Tuesday. However, when he got to the middle of the large, deserted lake, the wind stopped completely. He spent 20 hours and 35 minutes on his sailboat before he reached the beach near his cabin. What time did Jeremy make it back? _____ What day was it?_____

9. Driving at an average speed of 58 miles an hour, how long would it take you to travel 435 miles?_____

10. Write the fraction of the hour represented by the minutes listed below.

20 minutes _____   15 minutes _____
45 minutes _____   10 minutes _____
40 minutes _____   30 minutes _____

EXTRA!

Write the current time in both minutes and hours. Use fractions if needed.

Use Your Head!

Circle the better estimate.

Length		
a flagpole	10 m	10 m
a paperclip	30 mm	30 cm
a book	24 cm	24 m
a pencil	18 m	18 cm
a light switch	12 mm	12 cm
a cassette tape	90 m	90 cm

Weight		
a pen	14 mg	14 g
an apple	270 g	270 kg
a child	46 g	46 kg
a pin	130 mg	130 g
a baseball	145 g	145 kg
a watch	60 mg	60 g

Capacity		
a teaspoon	5 ml	5 l
a milk carton	1 l	1 kl
a hot tub	4 l	4 kl
a bucket	3 ml	3 l
a glass	180 ml	18 ml
a fish tank	15 l	15 kl

Temperature		
a hot bath	48° C	90° C
a cold drink	50° C	5° C
a very warm day	10° C	40° C
a cold winter day	−4° C	25° C
hot chocolate	80° C	50° C
ice cream	50° C	5° C

Good Guesswork

Circle the better estimate.

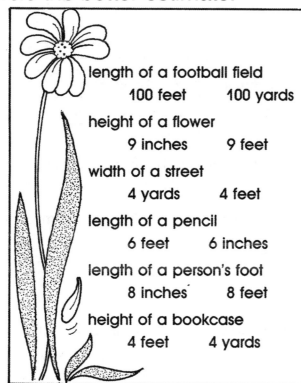

length of a football field
100 feet   100 yards

height of a flower
9 inches   9 feet

width of a street
4 yards   4 feet

length of a pencil
6 feet   6 inches

length of a person's foot
8 inches   8 feet

height of a bookcase
4 feet   4 yards

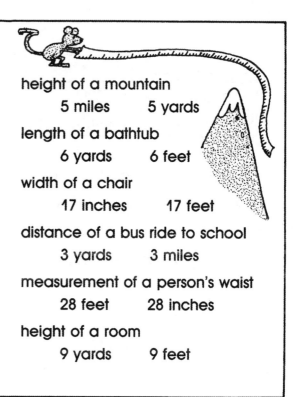

height of a mountain
5 miles   5 yards

length of a bathtub
6 yards   6 feet

width of a chair
17 inches   17 feet

distance of a bus ride to school
3 yards   3 miles

measurement of a person's waist
28 feet   28 inches

height of a room
9 yards   9 feet

Choose the best unit. Write mi., yd., ft., or in.

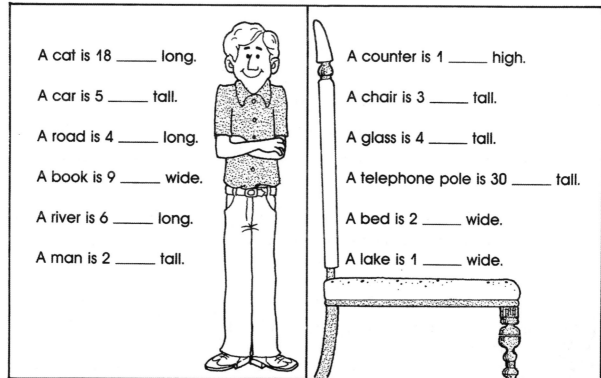

A cat is 18 _____ long.

A car is 5 _____ tall.

A road is 4 _____ long.

A book is 9 _____ wide.

A river is 6 _____ long.

A man is 2 _____ tall.

A counter is 1 _____ high.

A chair is 3 _____ tall.

A glass is 4 _____ tall.

A telephone pole is 30 _____ tall.

A bed is 2 _____ wide.

A lake is 1 _____ wide.

Name_____ Date_____

Linear Measurement

—1 CENTIMETER

12 inches (in.) = 1 foot (ft.)	10 millimeters (mm) = 1 centimeter (cm)
3 feet (ft.) = 1 yard (yd.)	100 centimeters (cm) = 1 meter (m)
5280 feet (ft.) = 1 mile (mi.)	1000 meters (m) = 1 kilometer (km)

1. Hillary had 2 feet of string. She cut off 5 inches of string. How much string did she have left? Write your answer in feet and inches. _____

2. David had 7 yards of rope. He used 4 yards 1 foot of rope for his tree house. How much rope was left? Write your answer in yards and feet. _____

3. Ten students ran a relay race. Each student ran 660 feet. What was the total distance of the race? Write your answer in miles and feet. _____

4. Amy made a poster for social studies class. She used 13 inches of blue string, 12 inches of green string, 15 inches of black string, and 14 inches of red string. What was the total amount of string she used? Write your answer in yards, feet, and inches. _____

5. A sheet of lined paper is 267 millimeters long and 201 millimeters wide. Give the length and width of the lined paper in centimeters and millimeters.

   Length = _____   Width = _____

6. A sheet of typing paper is 279 millimeters long and 216 millimeters wide. Give the length and width of the typing paper in centimeters and millimeters.

   Length = _____   Width = _____

7. Find the difference in the size of lined paper and typing paper. Give your answer in centimeters and millimeters.

   Difference in length = _____   Difference in width = _____

8. Brad is 155 centimeters tall. Give his height in meters and centimeters. _____

EXTRA! Find the distance between your desk and the teacher's desk. Write this number in both feet and inches.

Name _____ Date _____

Weight and Mass

16 ounces (oz.) = 1 pound (lb.)	1000 milligrams (mg) = 1 gram (g)
2000 pounds (lb.) = 1 ton (tn.)	1000 grams (g) = 1 kilogram (kg)

1. A chicken weighed 48 oz. How many pounds? _____

2. A turkey weighed 240 oz. How many pounds? _____

3. A bag of chocolate chips weighs 1 lb. 6 oz. How many ounces? _____

4. A loaf of bread weighs 1 lb. 8 oz. How many ounces? _____

5. Ellie the elephant weighed $6\frac{1}{2}$ tn. How many pounds? _____

6. At the Smithsonian Institution in Washington, D.C., there is a large stuffed African elephant.

   It weighed about 24,000 lb. when it was alive. How many tons did it weigh? _____

7. A small bat in Asia has a mass of 2208 mg. Give its mass in grams and milligrams. _____

8. A sea otter has a mass of 30 kg. Give its mass in grams. _____

9. A very large St. Bernard dog had a mass of 110,000 g.

   Its mass in kilograms is _____. This is about 295 lb.

10. A very small chihuahua had a mass of 995,000 mg.

    Its mass in grams is _____. This is about 2 lb.

11. A Belgian draft horse weighs 2200 lb. A small Shetland pony weighs 300 lb. What is the

    difference in their weight in pounds? _____ This about how many tons? _____

12. A recipe calls for 454 g of sugar. How many milligrams? _____

13. A can of peanuts has a mass of 226,000 mg. How many grams? _____

14. A box of crackers has a mass of 283 g. How many milligrams? _____

15. A box of biscuit mix has a weight of 2 lb. 8 oz. How many ounces? _____

16. A blue whale weighs about 119 tn. How many pounds? _____

Find the average weight of a dolphin using a book or the internet. Give its mass in kilograms and grams.

Name_____ Date _____

Looks Like Math

Temperature is measured in degrees. Temperatures may be measured on a Fahrenheit scale (F) or a Celsius scale (C).

**Water freezes at 32° Fahrenheit or 0° Celsius.
Water boils at 212° Fahrenheit or 100° Celsius.**

1. How many degrees difference is there between freezing and boiling

   a) on the Fahrenheit scale? _____ b) on the Celsius scale? _____

2. The usual human body temperature is about 99° Fahrenheit (F). a) This is how many

   degrees above freezing? _____ b) How many degrees below boiling? _____

3. The usual human body temperature is about 37° Celsius (C). a) This is how many

   degrees above freezing? _____ b) How many degrees below boiling? _____

4. A marathon runner's temperature may reach almost 106° F in hot weather.

   This is how many degrees greater than the runner's normal body temperature? _____

5. The marathon runner's temperature may reach 41° C. This is how many degrees greater than

   the runner's normal body temperature? _____

6. A woman was found in Chicago with a body temperature of only 61° F. At the hospital, her temper-

   ature returned to normal. a) How many degrees less than normal was this? _____ The woman's

   temperature was about 16° C. b) How many degrees less than normal was this? _____

7. The temperature in a sauna bath may reach 284° F. a) How many degrees above boiling is

   this? _____ b) This same sauna bath would have a temperature of about 140° C. How

   many degrees above boiling is this? _____

8. If your body temperature becomes too high you could die. A temperature of 10° F greater than

   the normal body temperature may be fatal. What body temperature is usually fatal? _____

9. A temperature of 6° C greater than the normal body temperature may be fatal.

   What body temperature is usually fatal? _____

EXTRA! When you are ill, the difference between your body temperature and your normal body temperature is called a fever. How many degrees of fever do you have if your body temperature is 102 degrees F?

Math's Borders

Solve each problem.

1. Sean ran around the outside of the playground. How far did he run?

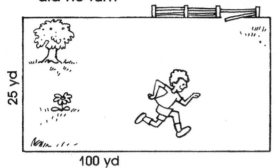

25 yd

100 yd

_____

4. How far is a drive from Hilltop to Carlyle to Plainview to Hilltop?

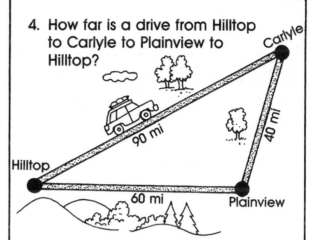

Carlyle

90 mi

40 mi

Hilltop

60 mi

Plainview

_____

2. LaKeesha framed her coin collection. How many inches of frame did she use?

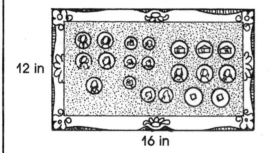

12 in

16 in

_____

5. Mrs. Garcia bound the edges of the latch hook rug she made with tape. How much tape did she use?

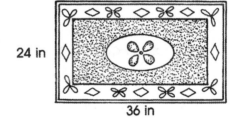

24 in

36 in

_____

3. The Jeffersons built a deck around their swimming pool. How many feet of material did they need?

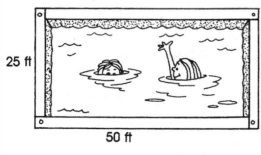

25 ft

50 ft

_____

6. Toni put fringe around her triangular scarf. How much fringe did she use?

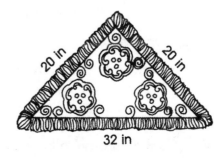

20 in

20 in

32 in

_____

Name_____ Date_____

Measuring the Cafeteria

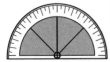

perimeter	area	length	width
sum	product	linear	square (sq.)

The **perimeter** of a region is the sum of the lengths of its sides. Perimeter is a linear measure. The **area** of a rectangular region is the product of its length and width. Area is measured in square units.

1. Some of the tables in the cafeteria are 3 ft. wide and 6 ft. long.

    a) What is the perimeter of one of these tables? _____ b) Find the area. _____

2. Some of the tables are 36 inches square.

    a) What is the perimeter? _____ b) What is the area? _____

3. The lid of the milk storage box is 2 ft. long and 4 ft. wide.

    a) Find the perimeter. _____ b) Find the area. _____

4. The lid of the ice cream box is 30 inches wide and 48 inches long.

    a) What is the perimeter? _____ b) What is the area? _____

5. The cafeteria is 72 ft. long and 50 ft. wide. a) The perimeter is _____. b) The area is _____.

6. A mural on the wall of the cafeteria is 3 yards high and 4 yards long.

    a) Its area is _____. b) Its perimeter is _____. c) Its perimeter is _____ feet.

7. A tray is 18 inches long and 14 inches wide.

    a) Find the perimeter. _____ b) Find the area. _____

8. Paper napkins are on each table. Each napkin is 10 inches wide and 12 inches long.

    a) Find the perimeter of 1 napkin. _____ b) What is its area? _____

9. Students return their trays through a window to the kitchen. The window is 36 inches wide and

    18 inches high. a) What is the perimeter? _____ b) What is the area? _____

10. Each light fixture on the ceiling is 1 foot wide and 4 feet long.

    a) What is the perimeter of a light fixture? _____ b) What is its area? _____

EXTRA! What is the area of your bedroom?

Math Graphs

Use the graphs to answer the questions.

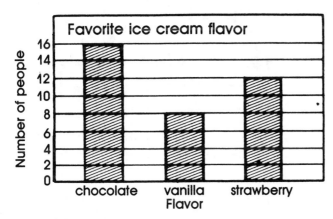

1. Which ice-cream flavor is liked by the most people? _____

2. How many more chose strawberry than vanilla? _____

3. How many people answered in the survey? _____

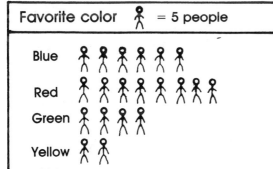

1. How many people chose red as their favorite color? _____

2. What percentage of the people surveyed chose yellow? _____

3. How many more people chose blue than green? _____

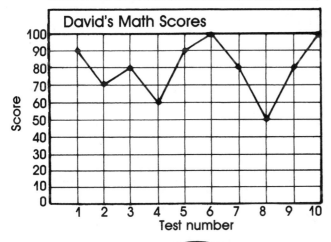

1. On which tests did David have a score of 100? _____

2. What was the lowest score David made on these ten tests? _____

3. What is David's average for these tests? _____

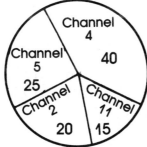

1. What percent of the people said they watched Channel 11 most often? _____

2. How many more people named Channel 4 than Channel 5? _____

3. What percent watched Channel 2 most often? _____

Great Graphs!

Graph the points and connect them in order. Name the figure.

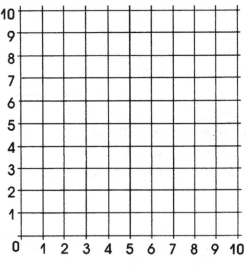

(2,1) → (8,1) → (8,7) → (2,7) →
(2,1)

Figure: _____

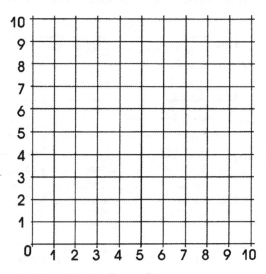

(3,2) → (6,2) → (8,5) → (6,8) →
(3,8) → (1,5) → (3,2)

Figure: _____

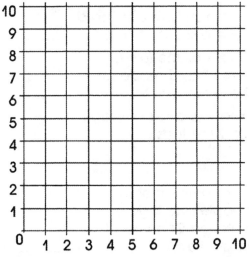

(2,3) → (6,10) → (10,3) → (2,3)

Figure: _____

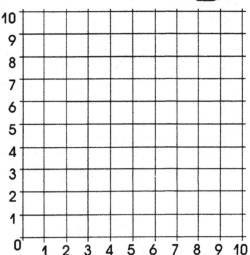

(1,3) → (1,6) → (3,8) → (6,8) →
(8,6) → (8,3) → (6,1) → (3,1) →
(1,3)

Figure: _____

Easier to Read

Construct line graphs from the information given below. You may find that using different colored lines will make your graphs easier to read. When your graphs are complete, answer the questions.

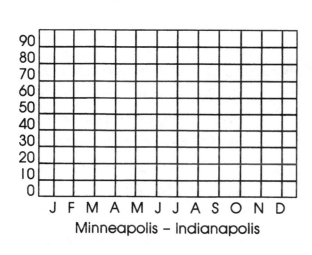

Minneapolis – Indianapolis

Month	Temperature °F			
	Minneapolis	Indianapolis	Des Moines	Boston
J	11	26	19	30
F	18	30	25	31
M	29	40	35	38
A	46	52	51	49
M	59	63	62	59
J	68	72	72	68
J	73	75	76	74
A	71	73	74	72
S	61	67	65	65
O	50	55	54	55
N	33	42	39	45
D	19	32	26	34

1. What is the difference between the highest and lowest temperatures for Indianapolis? _____ for Minneapolis? _____

2. What is the average temperature for June, in Indianapolis? _____ In Minneapolis? _____ What is the difference between the two? _____

3. What is the average yearly temperature for Minneapolis? (Round to the nearest whole number.) _____ for Indianapolis? _____ What is the difference between the two? _____

4. What is the highest average monthly temperature in Boston? _____ In Des Moines? _____

5. Which of those two cities has the lower average temperature in December? _____ How much lower? _____

6. What is the average monthly temperature for each city? (Round to the nearest whole number.)

_____

_____ What is the difference? _____

7. What average monthly temperature is the same for each city? Name the month in your answer. _____

Des Moines – Boston

Crossword Problems

Name _____ **Date** _____

Across:

3. Darla added 2.3, 0.06, and 1.9. What is the correct answer?

4. A transport truck was carrying 458 barrels of crude oil. After a small leak was found, it was determined 39 barrels had been lost. How many barrels remain?

5. Mr. Sanchez had 48 pepper plants in each of 12 rows. How many does he have in all?

7. How many years are in ten decades?

8. Mr. Shay's house lot is 36 yards wide. How wide is it in feet?

10. A race car averaged 162 miles per hour in a three-hour race. How many miles did it travel?

12. Jack multiplied 106 by nine and divided the answer by two. What is the correct final answer?

14. A total of 4,122 tickets were sold to an exhibition baseball game. The actual attendance was 3,275. How many people did not attend the game?

Down:

1. A log truck was hauling eight ton, 751 lb. of logs. How many pounds is this?

2. The population of a city was 65,280 before 920 people moved when a large company closed. What is the population now?

6. A computer company had exactly 6,542 units in stock after making a shipment of 458 to California. How many units did they have before the California shipment?

8. The school carnival sold 12 dozen donuts. How many donuts did they sell?

9. Of the 3,224 employees at a large office building, one-fourth drove their own cars. How many drove their own cars?

11. Sue needs to find one-third of 242,226. What is the answer?

12. An appliance store had 23 washing machines, 14 clothes dryers, and 63 television sets. They sold 15 television sets one Saturday. How many television sets are left?

13. Two yards and five inches would equal how many inches?

More Crossword Problems

Across:

2. Al has 43 toy soldiers. Jim has 48 and Mac has 54. How many toy soldiers belong to Jim and Mac?

4. Javier spent 34 of the 141 pennies he had saved. How many does he have left?

5. If 12 is multiplied by 12 and increased by 13, what is the answer?

7. A store had $1,235 in five-dollar bills at the close of the day. How many did they have?

9. Half of the 364 people entering a contest won pen sets. How many of them won pen sets?

10. Oats weigh 32 lb. per bushel. If Joy's horse ate seven bushels during a month, how many pounds did the horse eat?

12. The shipping weight of a chair is 36 lb. What is the shipping weight of nine of the chairs?

14. Workers picked 172 bushels of apples on Monday, 138 on Tuesday, and 164 on Wednesday. What was the total picked on the three days?

16. If 1,713 is divided by three and reduced by 91, what is the answer?

Down:

1. Mr. Samson sold one-fourth of the 2,000 pounds of cattle feed he had to a neighbor. How many pounds did he sell?

2. If 3,106 is added to 1,418 and the total is divided by four, what is the correct answer?

3. The electric company buried 909 yd. of cable. How many feet is this?

6. A truck was loaded with two tons plus 1,148 pounds of gravel. What is the weight in pounds?

7. For a music show, 1,078 people attended the first day, and 1,084 the next day. What was the total attendance?

8. The post office received 7,396 pieces of first class mail. They processed all but 132 by noon. How many did they process?

11. Kate worked three hours and 32 minutes for a neighbor. How many minutes did she work?

12. If 836 is multiplied by two, and the answer is multiplied by two, what is the final answer?

13. Mr. Markson drove 2,134 miles one month and 2,506 miles the next. What is the total miles he drove in the two months?

15. A bakery baked 65 dozen donuts for the town fair. How many donuts did they bake?

Tree Farm Trivia

1. If a tree is four years old and 2 feet in height, and it grows 1.5 feet per year, how tall will the tree be when it is 8 years old?_____

2. A big tree grower plans to sell 3,250 trees wholesale. A semi-trailer holds 500 trees. How many trucks will be needed?_____

3. The Aldrich Tree Farm sold one tree for $15.00, one wreath for $10.00, a tree bag for $1.50, and a tree stand for $14.00. Sales tax is 4 percent. What is the total bill to the customer?_____

4. If a row of trees is 1,000 feet long, and the trees are 5 feet apart in each row, how many trees are there in eight rows?_____

5. On the Aldrich Tree Farm, there are 35 pocket gophers, 10 deer, and 14 rabbits eating the tree seedlings. How many trees are left at the end of the year?
_____

6. An acre is 43,560 square feet. If the Christmas trees are planted in rows 8 feet apart, and the trees are 5 feet apart in the row, how many can be planted in one acre?_____

7. If it takes one man 2 minutes to shear a tree, how many hours will it take 3 men to shear 900 trees?_____

8. The local nursery will sell tree seedlings for $30 a hundred, or $150 for 1,000 trees. The Aldrich Farm wants to buy 750. Which would be the cheapest way to purchase the trees?_____

9. The Aldrich Farm hired 6 workers to shear the trees. Each worker was paid $4.00 per hour. Bill worked 6 hours, Jim 7.5 hours, Betty 9 hours, Tom 8 hours, Sally 4 hours, and Ron 6 hours. How much did the shearing cost?_____

10. A local church has a tree that is 15 feet tall. The janitor is six feet tall, and he can reach 2 feet above his head. How many feet up a step ladder must he climb to put a star on top of the tree?_____

What is your state tree? Write a few sentences about this type of tree.

Sue's Job Hunt

Dawn collects coins; she has several extra 1938 D pennies. She trades 3 of them for a nickel she needs. Then she finds a friend who will take 5 of them in trade for a dime. How many pennies does Dawn trade?

Basic Strategy:

1. Read the problem.	Read it.
2. Find the numbers.	Did you find 3 numbers?
3. Choose the operation.	You are looking for the total number of pennies that Dawn traded. You have to add all the pennies she traded.
4. Choose the numbers you need to work the problem.	There are 3 numbers; one is extra. Now you see why we included this step. The 1938 is extra. You need 3 and 5.
5. Solve the problem.	3 + 5 = 8

Study this example again; you will need to choose your numbers carefully. Every problem on this page will have an extra number.

Solve the following problems. Look carefully for any extra numbers.

1. In school, Sue is reading about occupations. She reads that secretaries can make $7.50 an hour after working 5 years, but that word-processing secretaries can make $9.75 an hour with the same experience. How much more per hour does a word-processing secretary make?

2. She calls Local #86 and finds that carpenters are paid $13.50 an hour when they work through the union. She knows that they work 40 hours a week. How much would a carpenter earn in a week?

3. Sue finds that 8 hamburger restaurants in town employ teenagers for part-time work. If she took a job, worked 15 hours during a week, and earned $50.25, how much would she be paid an hour?

4. While studying occupations, Sue learns that the government takes out part of your pay for income tax. Her father says nearly 19% of his hourly pay goes for taxes. If he earns $14.65 an hour and $2.80 is deducted for income tax, what is his hourly wage after taxes?

5. Finally, Sue learns about overtime. For example, a worker is paid 1 ½ times her salary if she works on Saturday. If an electrician earns $14.50 an hour and then makes a bonus of $7.25 an hour for overtime, how much does she earn altogether each hour?

The Paper Route

One of the most useful hints we can give for separating relevant and irrelevant information is **checking labels**. You've heard your teacher say, "Label your answers!" It is important. Watch how you can use labels to find the relevant and irrelevant information.

Dawn is 14 years old; her brother is 9 years old, but he is already 5 feet tall. How much older is Dawn than her brother?

If you read the problem, you know that you have to work a problem involving age. The important numbers should have age labels. Dawn is 14 years old; her brother is 9 years old. But the 5 talks about feet: her brother is 5 feet tall. That must be the irrelevant information. It doesn't have a label that fits the question. If you compare the question to the labels, you can often rule out one of the numbers. It's a good way to recognize the irrelevant information.

Read the following problems. Check the labels of each number.

1. Tammy delivers papers every morning; she takes a few minutes to read the paper before starting her route. On the morning of the 18th, she reads that her favorite college women's team won by the score of 97 points to 85 points. How many points were scored in the game?

2. Tammy has the largest route in town; she delivers 165 papers daily. The next largest route has 145 customers. If Tammy must collect $7 a month from each customer, how much will she collect in a month?

3. Earlier this year, Tammy's route was made smaller. Originally, she had 211 customers. After the route was changed, she had only 165 customers. How many customers did she lose?

4. Tammy earned a total of $1,980 last year. She thought that was pretty good for a 14-year-old girl. If she worked all 12 months, how much money did she earn each month?

5. Tammy's friend Scott also has a paper route. He has 142 customers. If Tammy earned $1,980 last year and Scott earned $1,704, how much more money did Tammy earn?

Crazy Collections

Solve each problem.

1. Jeff wants to have a rock from each of the 50 states in the United States. Jeff is 12 years old. If he already has rocks from 19 states, how many more rocks will Jeff have to get to finish his collection?

Relevant label:

2. When John went away to college, he divided his baseball card collection equally between his 2 younger brothers, who already had 800 baseball cards. If John had 900 cards in his collection, how many did each brother get?

Relevant label:

3. Barbara's collection of 14 Japanese dolls is worth $490. Last year her collection was worth $336. On the average, how much is each Japanese doll worth?

Relevant label:

4. Kevin had 135 model cars until he lost 49 of them when his family moved 1,300 miles from Philadelphia, Pennsylvania, to Tulsa, Oklahoma. How many cars did Kevin have left after the move?

Relevant label:

5. Jessica has 12 scratch-and-sniff stickers on each page of her sticker book. She has 16 stickers that smell like watermelon. If there are 14 pages in Jessica's sticker book and every page is full, how many stickers does she have?

Relevant label:

6. Ernie has 15 pet worms in his amazing worm collection. Ernie claims that 12 of his worms can sing and dance. If Ernie gets 29 more worms, how many will he have in his collection?

Relevant label:

Circle the extra information in each of the problems above.

The Cattle Caper

You will find that most of the key words which are used to identify addition problems can also be used with multiplication problems. In both cases, you are combining different sets to make a larger amount, so words like **together, altogether, in all,** or **total** will be used in both problem types. Asking another question is often helpful:

Are you combining different amounts? Are you combining two sets with two different amounts? If so, you add.

Are you combining several sets with the same amount? For example: Do you have four sets of twelve? If so, you **multiply**.

Remember it this way: If you're combining unequal amounts, you add. If you're combining equal amounts, then you multiply.

Try this hint with the following problems.

1. Reggie the Rustler rustles two herds in one night. If there were 287 cows in the first herd and 438 in the second, how many cows did Reggie rustle?

2. Reggie tries to sell his rustled cows at army posts. He stops at 14 different posts. If each cavalry outpost buys 35 cows, how many does Reggie sell?

3. Clem The Cook has to prepare steaks for 3 companies of cavalry. If there are 21 men in each company, how many steaks should Clem cook? (Cavalry men are limited to one steak each at Clem's post.)

4. Clem gets 210 pounds of hamburger and 320 pounds of steak from one critter. How many pounds of meat does Clem get from a cow?

5. When the sheriff finally catches up with Reggie The Rustler, he finds that Reggie has already sold 490 cows. If Reggie rustled 725, how many cows are left to return to their owners?

Camp Math

Joan tries to swim at least 100 yards every day of the year. During the 31 days in October, Joan managed to swim on 24 days. How many days did she miss?

> **Eliminating possibilities**: All word problems require that you select an operation to work the problem. Extra-number problems require that you eliminate some of the numbers in the problem. Let's see how you can do it.
>
> If you can't decide which numbers to use, try to see which number not to use. Read the example problem. It is about how many days Joan swims, not how far. You don't need to know that she swims 100 yards. You can eliminate the 100. It must be **extra**.

Solve the following problems by looking for ways to eliminate a number.

1. Jeremy went to Idaho to a summer camp when he was 13. The entire trip lasted 25 days. If Jeremy spent a total of 8 days driving to and from the camp, how long was he actually at camp?
Eliminate numbers:

2. A group of 18 campers spent a week on a pack trip along the Selway River and then up into the mountains. They followed the river for 65 miles, starting about Selway Falls. If each camper required 35 pounds of food on the trip, how many total pounds of food did the horses have to carry?
Eliminate numbers:

3. Jeremy's camp is located at an altitude of 1,240 feet above sea level. While on the 5-day packing expedition, the group climbed 6,340 feet higher into the mountains. How many feet did the group climb every day, on the average?
Eliminate numbers:

4. There were a total of 18 counselors and 270 boys at the camp, housed in 54 different tents. For all camp activities, the boys went with their own counselor. How many boys were in each group?
Eliminate numbers:

5. In July, a huge contest was organized to find the champion pie and cake eaters in the camp. The boys ate a total of 673 pieces of pie and 864 pieces of cake. The champion pie eater ate 17 pieces of pie. How many total desserts were eaten in the contest?
Eliminate numbers:

Once Upon a Time

1. Witch Hazel's recipe for frog stew calls for 5 fat bullfrogs and 2 bats' wings for each person who intends to feast on this rare delight. If Hazel is having 14 people for dinner, how many bullfrogs does she need for her stew?

2. Teratosaurus was a fierce meat-eating dinosaur who lived during the Triassic period over 150 million years ago. Teratosaurus weighed as much as 13 boys entering junior high school. If a junior high school boy weighs about 83 pounds, about how much did a Teratosaurus weigh?

3. Susan discovers some dinosaur eggs that are 80 million years old. If each egg weighs 13 ounces and the total weight of the eggs is 91 ounces, how many eggs did Susan discover?

4. Once upon a time, an army of brave knights attacked a fierce dragon. Unfortunately, the dragon was too fierce for the poor knights. He gobbled them up at the rate of 9 per minute. The dragon breathed fire and was 190 feet long. If there were 198 knights, how long did it take the dragon to devour them all?

5. Tim Toad weighed 146 grams before he ate some bugs for dinner. If the bugs weighed 49 grams and Tim ate them at the rate of 3 per minute, how much did Tim Toad weigh right after dinner?

6. The last dinosaur period, the Cretaceous period, began 135 million years ago. This was the era when giants like Triceratops and Tyrannosaurus Rex ruled the world. Tyrannosaurus was 50 feet long and had teeth as long as your foot. The Cretaceous period ended 65 million years ago. How long did the Cretaceous period last?

Use a book or other resource to find 5 facts about the Triceratops.

Building Math Skills

Drawing a picture might be helpful when working problems with extra numbers.

Problem:	**Solution:**	
Johnny has 9 quarters and 7 pennies. Billy	**Johnny**	**Billy**
has 12 quarters. How many quarters do Billy	Quarters (9)	Quarters (12)
and Johnny have in all?	Pennies (7)	

You are asked to combine the quarters. You can take out the row of pennies; that is **extra information**. You can tell it is extra a soon as you draw the picture.

Solve the following problems. Draw a picture when it helps.

1. Jim's report on carpenters is due on October 21. He reads that house size is measured in square feet of floor space; he finds a medium-size house plan with 1,792 square feeet of floor space. If a sheet of plywood covers 32 square feet, how many sheets of plywood will it take to cover the entire floor of the house?
Picture:

2. Jim reads that carpenters build a truss to make the ceiling and roof of a house. The truss for his plan is 32 feet long. The carpenter needs to make 26 trusses for the house. How many more does he have to make if he had made 18 already?
Picture:

3. A house is often priced in a figure called price per square foot. A house finished in 1984 might cost $32 a square foot. If a house has 1,250 square feet of floor space, how much would the house cost?
Picture:

4. The frame of a house is made of boards called studs. Each stud is about 8 feet long. A carpenter ordered 56 studs from the lumberyard when building the outside of the house and 78 more for the inside walls. How many studs did he use in all?
Picture:

5. Jim drew a simple house plan to see how a carpenter might plan. They house had 4 sides, all the same length. He figured that each wall would need 18 studs if each stud was placed 2 feet apart. How many studs did Jim's house need?
Picture:

Math is a Full-Time Job

1. A cabinetmaker finishes 3 cabinets that are all 4 feet high and made out of cherry wood. He sells all of them for a total profit of $732. How much profit does he make on each individual cabinet?

2. Karen drives a school bus 36 miles every school day. She gets paid $6.25 an hour. How far does Karen drive the school bus during October's 21 school days?

3. Last year Jack made $9.25 an hour working in a steel mill. Now he is making $10.35 an hour. How much will Jack be making next year if he gets a $2.17 an hour raise?

4. Gwen's secretary can type 75 words per minute. A typewritten page has about 225 words on it. How long will it take the secretary to type a 450-word letter?

5. The Pet Shoppe sold 17 parakeets on Saturday. There were 44 parakeets that were not sold. The Pet Shoppe also sold 11 puppies. How many parakeets did the pet store have when it opened on Saturday?

6. Jimbo has been a part-time clown for 19 years. He makes $45 when he appears at birthday parties. If Jimbo works at 17 parties during June, how much money does he make that month?

EXTRA! Create your own story problem using the numbers 73 and 272. Ask someone in your class to solve it.

Math Mountain

Key words or phrases can be helpful or they can mislead. The reason to look for a key word is to help find the action described in the problem. What actions are possible?

Addition: Combining two or more sets into one large set.

Subtraction: 1. Taking away part of any set.
2. Comparing the size of two sets.
3. Finding the missing part to make one set the same size as another.

Multiplication: Combining several sets of the same size into one large set.

Division: 1. Finding the size of several smaller sets when a large set is divided.
2. Finding how many smaller sets you can make from a larger set.

When solving a problem, you may find the key word helps describe the action, but sometimes it will not. The important idea is that in a story problem you should always look for one of the actions listed above.

Solve these problems. Does the key word help you to find the action?

1. Stacy's hobby is skiing. Her favorite mountain has a double ski lift. The first lift takes her 1,348 feet up the mountain, and the second takes her another 1,537 feet up the mountain. The two lifts take her how far up the mountain in all?

2. The mountain that Stacy skis on is 10,387 feet high. However, the top of the ski lift is only 7,586 feet high. How much higher is the mountain?

3. Stacy likes to ski so much that she bought a season ticket for the ski lift. The normal price for the lift is $8 a day. If the season ticket cost $225 and Stacy went skiing 45 times, what was the average price she paid for the ski lift?

4. The ski lift has little chairs where two people sit to ride up the mountain. Stacy usually rides with her father on the ski lift. If Stacy weighs 125 pounds with all of her ski equipment and her father weighs 218 with all of his equipment, how much weight is the chair carrying?

5. All five people in Stacy's family like to ski. One weekend they all went shopping for new ski outfits. If the jackets were priced at $95 and the ski pants were $125, how much would it cost the family if everyone bought a new ski jacket?

The Stamp Collection

Amber is a philatelist (stamp collector). She is also very interested in the American Civil War period, 1860-1865. Amber would like to have a complete collection of U.S. postage stamps issued during this period. Listed below is a chart showing some of the stamps and their approximate values.

Stamp	Color	Unused $ Value	Used $ Value
1 cent Franklin	Blue	40.00	8.00
2 cent Jackson	Black	45.00	11.00
3 cent Washington	Rose	11.00	1.50
5 cent Jefferson	Yellow	900.00	80.00
5 cent Jefferson	Brown	160.00	46.00
10 cent Washington	Green	55.00	9.00
12 cent Washington	Black	90.00	15.00
15 cent Lincoln	Black	132.00	22.00
24 cent Washington	Lilac	185.00	22.00
30 cent Franklin	Orange	120.00	17.50
90 cent Washington	Blue	310.00	63.00

1. Amber's grandmother has an old trunk filled with things that belonged to her grandmother, Amber's great-great-grandmother. While looking through the trunk, Amber discovers twelve unused 5-cent Jefferson stamps. The stamps are yellow. What is the total value of the stamps?

2. Amber also finds an unused 12-cent Washington which is worth two times as much as another stamp from this period. Which stamp is it?

3. How much more valuable is the 30-cent Franklin stamp unused than used?

4. Amber takes $200 to buy a stamp. If she has $15 left over, which stamp did she buy?

5. Amber finds two unused 15-cent Lincoln stamps and sells one of them. How many used 2-cent Jackson stamps could she buy with the money?

Mountain Men Math

1. **Guess and check**. With this strategy, you guess a reasonable answer first, then work the problem. Finally, you check to see if your guess checks with the actual answer.

2. **Draw a picture**. Have you tried to make a diagram or a picture about a problem recently? Did it help? It often will, so remember this hint.

These hints or strategies you have learned before. Don't stop using them. They are often helpful in solving problems.

1. The mountain men were the first American settlers who explored the West. They often went into the Western wilderness searching for beaver pelts. If a mountain man trapped 235 beaver pelts and received $3 for each pelt when he returned to St. Louis, how much money did he make?

2. Once each year the mountain men would gather for a rendezvous near the Green River in Wyoming. If 28 trappers came from Montana, 47 from Colorado, and 36 from Wyoming, how many men gathered at the rendezvous?

3. A mountain man might pile his pelts into a canoe and float down the Missouri River to St. Louis to sell the pelts. If he traveled an average of 40 miles a day, how many days would it take to make the trip? (His total trip was 1,520 miles.)

4. A mountain man might spend an entire winter high in the Rocky Mountains, trapped in his cabin during severe snowstorms. If the trapper started with 45 pounds of venison and ate 27 pounds before the snow let up, how much of the venison was left?

5. The mountain men collected beaver pelts so that people in American and European cities could wear beaver hats. If a store owner bought 150 beaver hats and sold each one for $8, how much money did he receive?

18 Holes of Math

Have you noticed that there are many different words which suggest combining sets (addition) or finding how much is left over (subtraction)? Review this list of some of the possible words.

Some Key Words for Addition
total
altogether
together
in all

Some Key Words for Subtraction
left
left over
difference
remains
less than

Any of these words may be used to suggest addition or subtraction as the operation to be used in a problem.

Work the following problems, looking for the key words. This time the words won't appear in bold print.

1. Todd plays on the golf team. During the first tournament, he hit the ball 218 yards on his first shot and 165 yards on his second shot. What was the total distance of both shots?

2. Todd was angry on a short hole. He hit a poor shot which only traveled 78 yards. If the hole was 142 yards long, how much of the distance remained for Todd's second shot?

3. On the first day, Todd's score was 87; on the second day, his score was 95. What was his total score for the tournament?

4. On the second day, Todd shot a score of 95 while his friend Sam shot 86. What was the difference between their scores?

5. On the golf course's longest hole, Todd hit the ball hard three times straight. If the ball traveled 175 yards each time, how far had it traveled after all of the shots?

Math Makes a Great Pet

1. The common iguana is a bright green lizard with a little blue on its head and neck. The average length of an iguana is 60 inches. If Izi has a pet iguana that is 32 inches long, how much shorter is this than the average?

2. The ideal temperature range for a pet iguana is from 78°F to 91°F. What is the difference between the ideal low and high temperatures for this lizard?

3. Among the best foods for lizards are crickets. If your pet lizard ate 13 crickets each day, how many would it eat in 7 days?

4. Mike has 59 crickets in a cage. They multiply very quickly. If Mike puts in 11 more crickets, how many will he have?

5. Bloodsuckers are lizards that get their strange name from their ability to turn their heads a bright red color. These lizards live in the forests of India and are harmless. If you had 12 bloodsuckers and bought 14 more, how many would you have in all?

6. The desert iguana is light brown with spots and lives in the American Southwest. An interesting thing about this creature is that it can't digest food unless the temperature is 90°F or higher. If you had a desert iguana in a cage with a temperature of 74°F, how many degrees would you have to add to the cage temperature before the iguana could eat?

 EXTRA!

Name another type of lizard commonly kept as a pet.

Name_____ Date_____

Dan Goes to College

The key word in a problem helps suggest the operation you must choose. For addition, key words suggest combining two sets to form a larger set. But there are three different situations which suggest subtraction as an operation and they all have different key words. Study these three situations.

1. **Take away**. This problem type requires that you take away part of a set. Key words for this problem type are similar to **left** or **left over** or **remaining**.

2. **Comparison**. This problem type requires that you compare two amounts and find how much larger one is than the other. Key words for this problem type are **difference** or **how much larger** or **how much less**.

3. **Missing Amount**. This problem type requires that you find how much should be added to one set to make it as large as another set. (Example: If you want to buy something for $6 and only have $4, how much more money do you need?) Key words for this problem type are **how much more** or **how many more**.

Let's try some problems. You will find all of the various subtraction problems in this set of problems. But be aware, some are not subtraction problems.

1. Dan was amazed at how much he had to read in college. His psychology class required a textbook of 784 pages and a readings book with 932 pages. How many more pages were in the readings book?

2. "These books are expensive," Dan thought as he looked at a chemistry book that cost $48. If Dan only had $25 with him, how much more did he need to buy the chemistry book?

3. Dan's English class requires that he read 8 American novels. If the price of each novel is $12, how much does Dan have to pay for the books?

4. Even Dan's sailing class required reading. He had to read a book on sailing techniques (cost: $9.70) and a book on safety (cost: $7.25). What was the total price for both books?

5. Finally, Dan found that his chemistry class required a lab manual. He took $20 and ran to the bookstore just before the class. If the book cost $12.75, how much of his money was left over?

Name_____ Date _____

Money Math

1. Last July Bill and Martha opened up a lemonade stand in their neighborhood. The kids decided they could make money since the temperature had hit a record of 108°F. The old record was 97°F. What was the difference between the old record and the new record?

2. Bill went to the supermarket to buy lemons, sugar, and paper cups. Bill had $23 with him. If the supplies cost $7, how much money did Bill have left?

3. Martha's job was to build the lemonade stand and work on the advertising. Martha figured it would take her 7 hours to get her work finished. After 3 hours, how much longer would Martha have to work to finish the stand and advertising?

4. Bill had bought 75 lemons at the store. If Martha and Bill used 19 lemons to make their first batch of lemonade, how many lemons remained?

5. The kids sold 14 cups of lemonade the next morning and 3 times as much in the hot afternoon. How many cups of lemonade did they sell in the afternoon?

On the back of this paper, create a poster that Bill and Martha could use to attract customers to their lemonade stand. Be sure to include the 5Ws and H (who, what, when, where, why, and how).

The Old West

1. Boot Hill, the outlaws' graveyard, gets 4 new residents each week. What would be the total number of new graves in 52 weeks?

2. Dead-Eye Jones is the fastest gun in the West. Unfortunately, he can't shoot straight. During target practice, Dead-Eye accidentally shoots flying ducks, windows, and old trashcans. Last month Dead-Eye had to pay $265 in damages. This month his bill is only $91. What is Dead Eye's total damage for both months?

3. Sharon and Bill add 65 new head of cattle to their herd. They already had 177 cattle. How many head of cattle do they have altogether?

4. It costs Black Bart 19 cents to have the blacksmith put a new shoe on his horse. What would be the total cost of having all 4 shoes done?

5. At the Cactus Flats pie-eating contest, the 12 contestants ate an average of 6 pies each. How many pies were eaten altogether during the contest?

6. Buffalo Bull fired 16 cowboys who worked for him. If Buffalo Bull had 41 cowboys working for him, how many does he have left?

Write a few sentences explaining why cowboys wore chaps. Use the internet or an encyclopedia.

Calculator Entry

To enter 12 x 4 + 5 x (3+7) into the calculator, press

| 12 | x | 4 | + | 5 | x | (| 3 | + | 7 |) | = |

For the problems below, write the keystrokes in the boxes required to enter each problem into the calculator. Then enter it and find the answer.

1. 10 x 2 + 3 x (1 + 5) = _____

2. 8 x 4 + 1 x (3 + 3) = _____

3. (6 + 2) x (3 + 5) = _____

4. ((9 + 3) ÷ 2) x 6 = _____

5. 9 x 6 + 3 = _____

6. 9 x (6 + 3) = _____

Use your calculator to create a math problem using addition, subtraction, and multiplication. Use parentheses in the appropriate places.

Counting on the Calculator

Can you count by 9's on the calculator and stop on 261?
Here's how. (The calculator keystrokes used here are for a *TI-30* calculator. Your calculator may have different keystrokes.)

Press [9] [+] [K] [=] [=] [=] ...on your calculator until 261 appears.

1. Why does this work? _____

    _____

2. Can you count by 9's on the calculator and stop at 114? _____
    Why? _____

Press [4] [+] [9] [K] [=] [=] [=] ...on your calculator.

3. What happens? _____

Press [9] [+] [4] [K] [=] [=] [=] ...on your calculator.

4. What happens? _____

5. Call 9 our addend and 4 our start number. What start number less than 9 would you need to stop on 116? _____

6. Count by 7 on your calculator. What are the keystrokes? _____

7. Let 7 be our addend and 5 our start number. Pressing the [=] key 6 times gives what answer? _____

8. Is it possible to stop on 82? _____ Why? _____

9. Is it possible to stop on 90? _____ Why? _____

10. How many times do you have to press the [=] key to stop on 110? _____
    Why? _____

Performance Night

Each year the students at New City School entertain their parents with programs of music and dramatics.

1. In the school band there are 6 trumpet players, 4 trombone players, 12 clarinet players, 4 flute players, 2 bass players, and 3 drummers. Find the total number of students in the band. _____

2. In the school orchestra there are 16 violin players, 4 cello players, 2 bass players, 4 clarinet players, 2 flute players, 2 trumpet players, 3 French horn players, and 1 drummer. Find the total number of students in the orchestra. _____

3. The fifth-grade chorus has 16 boys and 17 girls. How many students are in the fifth-grade chorus? _____

4. The sixth-grade chorus has 27 boys and 24 girls. How many students are in the sixth-grade chorus? _____

5. Find the total number of fifth and sixth graders who sing in a chorus. _____

6. How many more sixth graders sing in a chorus than fifth graders? _____

7. The fourth-grade class did choral readings. Nineteen students had high voices and 16 students had low voices. How many fourth graders were in the program? _____

8. The students presented the program in a school assembly to 51 kindergartners, 46 first graders, 48 second graders, and 37 third graders. How many students saw the program? _____

9. There are 320 students in New City School. If 119 students performed in the assembly and 19 students were absent, how many students were in the audience? _____

10. For Performance Night the chairs in the auditorium were put in 25 rows with 20 chairs in each row. How many chairs? _____

11. The parent association made 648 cookies for the students who performed. Each student ate 3 cookies. How many students were in the performance? _____

List the type of instruments commonly included in an orchestra. List them in alphabetical order.

It's Party Time!

Menu: 12" pizzas and soda   Budget: $40.00

1. How many 8 oz. servings of soda can you get from 4-32 oz. bottles?

_____

2. Pizza Palace will deliver the pizzas. Two pepperoni pizzas cost $6.25 each. Three Canadian bacon pizzas cost $6.50 each. One pizza with everything costs $7.00. Total bill?_____

3. Each pizza serves two people. How many people will be served? _____

4. Average cost per serving for the people. (See problems 2–3.) _____

5. Eight 16 oz. bottles of soda cost $1.92. One 64 oz. bottle costs $1.60. Which costs less per ounce? _____ How much less?_____

6. Full price frozen pizzas cost $3.89. How much will the pizza cost on Double Value Coupon Day?_____

7. Make your own! Figure the costs.

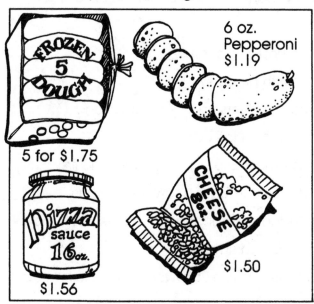

6 oz.
Pepperoni
$1.19

5 for $1.75

$1.56

$1.50

35¢ cents OFF REGULAR PRICE !! 35¢
coupon

Pizza for Two

$\frac{1}{2}$ loaf frozen dough = $_____

1 cup (8 oz.) pizza sauce = $_____

6 oz. pepperoni = $_____

8 oz. cheese, grated = $_____

Total Cost = $_____

8. How much will the cost be per person for 12 people? Round your answer to the nearest hundredth._____

EXTRA!

On the back of this page, create a menu for Pizza Palace. Be sure to include prices and any "specials" you have.

Page 3

30	16	48	21	
56	24	45	18	
33	36	19	23	24
28				
268	207	239	239	154
141				
168	148	284	141	327
241				

Page 4

1110;   1667;

1916;   1228;   1649;   1874;   1958;   2213;

2207;   2529;   2260;   2045;   2494;   1329;

12,591;   15,140;   19,107;   18,580;   16,734

16,848;   18,814;   18,578;   12,822;   16,215

Page 5

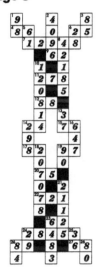

Page 6

28	25	27	33			
44	18	29	9	48	19	19
79	48	55	36	25	25	48
11	48	77	27	59	38	12
66	15	16	37	57	32	39
37	59	47	41	23	39	68
54	27	15	13	22	46	39
19	53	68	26	17	34	

Page 7

2	1	17	1	51	18	25
41	11	36	51	20	64	52
30	20	33	10	33	6	13
24	20	22	54	42	8	35
53	13	50	5	3		
20	32	72	84	70	16	4

Page 8

6498	956			
1357	857	3225		
989	1748	5999	112	5829
2781	1627	4889	1891	1389
4876	8395	3459	2187	4681
2482	2891	2926	6287	1599
59	890	1057	3938	2650

Page 9

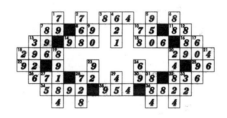

Page 10

551,244; 116,880
154,616; 334,248
4,000,000; 2,725,816; 2,749,110; 4,661,718
1,083,183; 992,142; 2,180,750; 1,582,032
5,803,707; 1,147,704; 239,994; 6,021,195

Page 11

183,708			
236,820	165,000		
140,000	252,456	17,968	198,891
195,750	125,496	612,000	98,366
176,580	332,160	27,264	587,574

Page 12

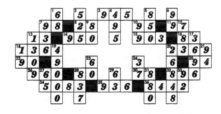

Page 13

Page 14

2, 2, 3, 3, 9
3, 2, 6, 2, 2, 2, 4
2, 5, 2, 2, 4
3, 2, 3
3, 5, 15
3, 7, 21
2, 2, 7, 5, 35
17, 3
2, 2, 4, 2, 3
3, 3, 9, 3, 27
Prime Numbers – 53, 79, 7, 41, 53, 71

Page 16

6
5, 8, 4
27, 13, 3
6, 7, 3
16, 6, 9

Page 17

2		
1	3	4
4	3	2
5	7	6
5	4	7

Page 18

12		
30	12	42
24	24	40
10	6	20
30	9	35

Page 19

36
30, 48, 140
72, 135, 45
22, 72, 44
75, 140, 210

Page 20

23	19			
13	12			
13	13	31	10	28
29				
21	114	70	53	134
1010	620	212	220	421

Page 21

24	10		
17	41	34	31
21	13	101	110
118	67	322	83

Page 22

49	
78	92
318	630
547	909

Page 23

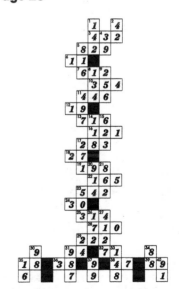

Page 24

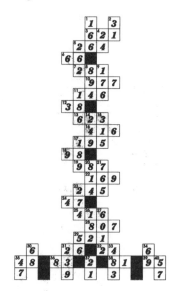

Page 25

A. C, S, V
B. V, C, S
C. V, C, S, C, C, V
D. 2 1/8, 4 2/3, 1 2/9, 4 1/6, 1, 2, 3 1/7, 1 1/8
E. 9/2, 17/3, 33/5, 21/8, 43/7, 33/10, 40/6, 7/5

Page 27

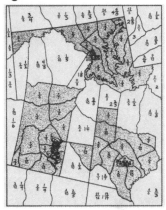

Page 29

43	35		
36	68		
21	53	15	35
32	33	62	7
11	19	7	53
29	17	10	15
33/5	53/9	21/2	24/5
83/8	49/6	29/10	17/7
83/12	65/12	77/10	43/8
25/4	22/7	33/8	65/12

Page 30

9 ÷ 8 = 1 1/8; 8 ÷ 5 = 1 3/5
35 ÷ 5 = 7; 77 ÷ 8 = 9 5/8
7 ÷ 2 = 3 1/2; 96 ÷ 8 = 12; 63 ÷ 9 = 7; 25 ÷ 9 = 2 7/9
10 ÷ 2 = 5; 13 ÷ 4 = 3 1/4; 15 ÷ 8 = 1 7/8; 10 ÷ 10 = 1
33 ÷ 11 = 3; 56 ÷ 5 = 11 1/5; 19 ÷ 6 = 3 1/6; 52 ÷ 4 = 13
56 ÷ 7 = 8; 43 ÷ 3 = 14 1/3; 73 ÷11 = 6 7/11; 37÷12 =3 1/12
17 ÷ 10 = 1 7/10; 54 ÷ 9 = 6; 16 ÷ 9 = 1 7/9; 21 ÷ 4 = 5 1/4
21 ÷ 8 = 2 5/8; 65 ÷ 7 = 9 2/7; 36 ÷ 12 = 3; 15 ÷ 3 = 5
51 ÷ 4 = 12 3/4; 21 ÷ 2 = 10 1/2; 66 ÷ 11 = 6; 30 ÷ 3 = 10
18 ÷ 3 = 6; 20 ÷ 9 = 2 2/9; 19 ÷12 =1 7/12; 13÷ 6 =2 1/6

Page 31

1. 1/7 + 5/6 = 41/42
2. 2/8 + 5/6 = 1 1/12
3. 5/3 + 9/7 > 2, 9/3 + 5/7 > 2, 9/3 + 7/5 > 2,
   5/9 + 7/3 > 2, 9/5 + 3/7> 2, 9/7 + 5/3 > 2,
   9/5 + 7/3 > 2
4. 4/2 + 8/6 > 3, 8/2 + 4/6 > 3, 8/2 + 6/4 > 3,
   6/2 + 4/8 > 3, 6/2 + 8/4 > 3, 6/4 + 8/2 > 3,
   8/6 + 4/2 > 3
5. 1/15 + 2/16

Page 32

1 2/5; 1 7/12
3/4; 1
1 1/5; 4/17; 7/10; 13/15
8/11; 1; 1 1/2; 1 2/11
1 1/4; 1/2; 11/14; 7/12
9/10; 7/9; 1/3; 1 2/15
1 1/3; 1 3/4; 1; 1 4/9
15/22; 7/8; 6/7; 11/15
12/25; 1 5/8; 4/5; 5/6
2/3; 1 2/7; 5/8; 11/12

Page 33

1. 5/12
2. 1 1/6
3. 7/8
4. 1 1/10
5. 1 1/10
6. 11/15
7. 2/5
8. 3/4
9. 5/18
10. 3
11. 1 3/5
12. 1/3
13. 4/7
14. 1
15. 1 1/5

Page 34

1 1/4; 13/15
1 1/10; 5/6; 2/3
1 1/9; 8/9; 1 3/16; 1 1/2
15/16; 5/8; 1 2/15; 1 1/12
11/14; 1 1/16; 1/2; 1 1/4

Page 35

19 5/6; 18 5/8; 15 3/4
26 4/5; 26 1/10; 14 9/10
12 2/3; 28 1/8; 12 3/5; 16 3/10; 25 1/2
11 1/2; 12 2/7; 24 1/3; 10 1/5; 17 3/7
25 1/4; 34 1/6; 29 7/8
20 1/3; 37 2/3; 35 1/5
30 3/5; 28 3/8; 21 1/2

Page 36

6 1/2; 9 1/3; 3 2/7
7; 5; 5 1/2
8; 2 4/5; 2 1/2; 1 3/8; 3 1/2
7 1/6; 5 1/10; 10 7/8; 10 1/4
3 1/9; 4 3/10; 7 1/2; 13 1/3

Page 37

1. 4 1/2
2. 4 3/8
3. 13
4. 8 4/5
5. 3 3/7
6. 10 2/7
7. 10 1/2
8. 8 3/4
9. 5 2/3
10. 8
11. 19 1/3
12. 23 1/8
13. 39 1/10
14. 112 2/9
15. 69 3/10
16. 84 3/8
17. 32
18. 25 9/10
19. 27 5/9
20. 5 3/10
21. 14 3/4
22. 24 1/8
23. 192 17/30
24. 14 1/8
25. 110 1/2
26. 79 11/18
27. 14 11/12
28. 145 23/24

Page 38

72 3/8	21 5/12		
31 1/2	28 1/2	20 2/3	22 5/6
93 7/8	140 3/8	27 1/12	22 1/6
27 1/9	117 5/8	39 1/3	68 2/5
86 7/8	26 23/24	68 11/12	72 9/10

Page 39

25 1/5
21 3/4	20 3/8	19 5/8	22 7/10
24 7/12	24 11/16	127 9/16	44 13/16
116 1/4	73 7/8	129 13/16	126 5/6
144 1/8	179 1/2	106 5/12	56 5/6

Page 40

1. 4/5
2. 1/4
3. 2/3
4. 1
5. 1/6
6. 2/3
7. 3/5
8. 1/2
9. 1/4
10. 1/2
11. 1 1/8
12. 1/2
13. 1 1/4
14. 1/9
15. 9/10
    9 squares

Page 41

1. 19/30
2. 7/8
3. 1/2
4. 1 1/10
5. 1 1/16
6. 8/9
7. 1 5/12
8. 9/10
9. 1
10. 1/2

1. 1/10
2. 1/4
3. 2/5
4. 1/6
5. 11/40
6. 1/6
7. 1/6
8. 3/10
9. 1 3/24
10. 1/3
11. 5/7
12. 2/9
13. 11/20
14. 1/5
15. 5/12

Page 42

16	9	7			
15	2	17			
8	3	11;	15	4	11
9	8	1;	4	7	11
0	6	7;	3	2	5
0	6	1;	4	5	9
6	1;	9	4	5	
10	8;	8	5	3	
6	11;	3	8		
9	5	14;	2	1	

Page 43

1 1/2	6/11	4/15	1 1/3
5/7	4/7	1/4	1/10
5/8	1/3	1/9	5/8
11/12	1/16	1 7/15	1/4
1 3/20	1/2	7/8	11/12

Page 44

A. 10
B. 4 2/3
C. 8
D. 4 1/2
E. 5 1/3
F. 3 4/5
G. 5 1/4
H. 11 3/4
I. 6 1/6
J. 19 3/8
K. 16 7/15
L. 18 3/8
M. 7 13/14
N. 10 1/6
O. 3 3/5
P. 6 7/10
Sum = 34

Page 45

3/8; 4/21
8/21; 3/8; 5/18
7/18; 7/30; 1/5; 5/24
4/15; 1/3; 1/3; 5/36

Page 46

1. 1/4
2. 1/10
3. 3/5
4. 5/8
5. 1/6
6. 1/9
7. 1/4
8. 0
9. 2/9
10. 3/10
11. 1/3
12. 1/10
13. 1/2
14. 1/4
15. 1/7
16. 1/4
17. 2/5
18. 1/2
19. 1/3
20. 2/5

Page 47

3/4; 3/4
4/5; 1/3; 2/3; 5/6
5/9; 3/10; 7/13; 2/3
3/4; 1/2; 1/3; 2/5
3/5; 1/2; 1/3; 1/7
1/5; 2/3; 5/8; 1/2; 3/5; 4/7
3/10; 2/9; 1/3; 3/5; 1/3; 1/12

Page 48

2/7	7/9		
3/10	4/9		
7/15	1/3		
3/5	1/7		
2/7	2/15	3/8	2/7
4 3/5	1 1/2	7 1/3	5/7
1 3/7	2 1/5	8 1/5	2 4/5
3 2/7	14 1/4	7 1/3	7 8/9

Page 49

4 7/8	3 7/10	1 7/8	3 7/12
2 9/10	2 3/4	2 1/2	5 1/2
2 4/5	1 1/2	4 5/6	1 2/3
2 7/9	1 7/8	2 13/14	3/8

Page 50

10 1/3; 8
9 2/9; 7 1/7; 3 1/8
4 1/5; 5 1/4; 5 3/8; 4 7/10; 6 1/6
8 1/2; 5 3/4; 6 7/12
6 1/2; 9 5/7; 3 5/8
2 3/5; 7 2/3; 1 9/10

Page 51

1 3/5	2 5/6	5 1/3	1 9/10
3 7/10	7 7/9	1/2	1 1/4
3 11/12	4 5/8	2 2/3	4 4/5
6 1/2	3 3/5	4 5/6	2 9/14

Page 52

38 2/7	1/3	2 3/4	
3 1/2	7 3/5	4 1/2	6 1/2
1 8/9	7 1/4	8 1/2	4 1/2
3 9/10	11 3/10	2 11/14	5 5/6

Page 53

3 3/5	3 4/7		
7 1/2	1 5/7	3 4/5	5 2/5
12 2/3	6 1/2	4/5	3 1/2
12 1/4	18 2/3	3/7	4 3/7

Page 54

14 1/4	50 2/3	3 1/8
5 3/10	38 1/3	4 19/20
1 2/3	8 3/5	8 8/15	3 5/6
10 5/8	3 2/3	1 2/3	8 1/2

Page 55

81 1/4	7 5/6	7 4/5	6 3/7
21 5/6	7 3/7	2 3/5	4 1/2
4 3/5	2 5/8	13/16	1 13/14
82 2/3	9/10	3 2/5	1 3/4
3 4/9	17 3/4	1 3/5	2 2/7
3 4/5	9 11/12	3 4/5	9 3/4

Page 56

7 5/6; 3 4/9; 5 3/4
2 1/3; 3 3/5; 6 1/2
10 9/10; 8 3/10; 8 5/9; 15 7/9
3 2/3; 10 1/3; 1 7/8; 4 3/8
3 11/12; 14 1/4; 9 6/7; 3 3/5

Page 57

7/12	5/32	2/27	
3/10	2/11	4/9	1/5
5/7	1/8	1/3	3/44
2/9	3/22	1/15	3/7
1/30	3/4	3/8	1/4
1/15	10/27	2/5	7/30
1/4	1/12	1/4	1/6
1/12	1/3	1/10	

Page 58

36; 3
8; 5
4; 3; 6
1; 11; 2
25; 8; 59
10; 8 1/3
8 1/2; 3
6 2/3; 24
12 1/2; 21
9; 6

Page 59

(Beginning in upper-left corner of each circle)
3, 3 1/8, 4 1/12, 12 3/5, 2 3/5
12 3/8, 6, 11 1/5, 5 5/12, 2 1/16
8 4/5, 6 1/2, 4 7/12, 1 1/3, 3
3 1/28, 1 1/3, 2 4/11, 3 5/7, 2 4/5
3 2/11, 5 13/24, 5, 4 1/4, 4 22/27

Page 60

3 3/7, 2 4/7
16/25, 8/15
1 5/6, 5 1/2
2 1/7, 1 7/8
2 5/8, 2 1/4
7/12, 1 1/6

Page 61

1/5 = 1/40
1/4 = 1/48
1/2 x 1/2 = 1/4
1/8 x 1/6 = 1/48; 1/3 x 1/8 = 1/24
1/7 = 1/28; 1/2 = 1/10
1/6 = 1/42; 1/3 = 1/18
1/10 x 1/3 = 1/30; 1/9 x 1/3 = 1/27
1/5 x 1/5 = 1/25; 8 = 27
3 = 21; 4 = 8
2 = 8; 10 = 110
6 = 120; 15 x 3 = 45
21 x 4 = 84; 29 x 2 = 58

Page 62

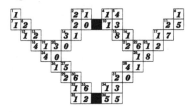

Page 63

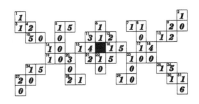

Page 64

1. 3/10
2. 8/9
3. 5/12
4. 3/7
5. 1/3
6. 2/8 or 1/4
7. 2/5
8. 3/6 or 1/2
9. 1/4
10. 3/4
11. 3/10

Page 65

1. Annie - $30.00, Lyndi - $35.00
2. 7/8 of assignment
3. 28 1/2 minutes
4. 1 1/2 hrs-5 7/12 hrs
5. 4 2/7 miles-21 3/7 miles
6. 3/4, 7/9, 3/5, 5/6, 1/3
7. 1 5/8 lbs
8. 11 5/8 lbs

Page 66

1. 1/3, 1/2, 2/2, or 1
2. 2000
   3000, 1000
   5000, 4000
3. 1/4, 1/2, 3/4
4. 1500, 3000, 4500
5. 12 min, 18 min, 24 min, 36 min
6. 2/3, 1/3
7. 3 tapes, 2/3 left

Page 67

1. 5 runners
2. 62 girls
3. 9 3/4 minutes
4. 51 1/2 minutes
5. 12 feet
6. 198 feet
7. 31 cans; $15.50; $4.50

Page 68

1. 1/6
2. $1.50
3. 2/5
4. $4.50
5. $1.20
6. Ed; $0.15 or 15¢
7. $2.25
8. $1.50
9. $90
10. $35; $70; $28; $7

Page 69

1. 3/10
2. 2/15
3. 1/3
4. 4/21
5. 1/10
6. 3/8
7. 1/4
8. 1/24
9. 1/32
10. 5/9

Page 70

25%, 20%, 36%
75%, 37%, 50%
10%, 19%, 60%
30%, 15%
80%, 48%
NINETEEN DOLLARS

Page 71

A. 0.36	1.36	1.205	0.1210	6.44
B. 4.32	5.460	12.12	44.668	3.752
C. 0.006	0.32	0.096	0.0030	0.09
D. 0.18	0.00040	0.040	0.00280	0.10
E. 0.0032	0.084	0.024	0.00004	0.024

Page 72

A. 0.8 / 0.04
B. 0.08 / 0.4
C. 0.80 / 0.40

D. 6/100 – 3/10
E. 6/100 – 30/100
F. 6/10 – 3/100

G. 0.45 / 0.11 / 7.30 / 12.10
H. 0.60 / 0.15 / 5.60 / 28.40
I. 0.05 / 0.13 / 1.40 / 3.04
J. 0.29 / 0.20 / 8.04 / 9.03
K. 0.13 / 0.01 / 6.05 / 9.30

L. 1/5, 3/4, 9/10, 1/20
M. 1/4, 3/10, 3/25, 7/20
N. 6 1/4, 2 1/2, 6 1/5, 3 1/4
O. 37/100, 31/50, 7 7/10, 4 3/25
P. 7/25, 5 3/4, 9/20, 3 3/5

Page 73

Page 74

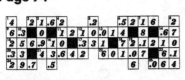

Page 75

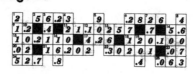

Page 76

9.3; 0.7; 11.9
0.8; 7.6; 0.9; 1.20
0.38; 7.69; 10.59; 34.61; 59.65
0.2; 6.5; 0.1; 2.8; 0.3
3.9; 3.0; 0.4; 0.78; 0.11
2.71; 0.45; 0.02; 3.16; 0.21

Page 77

5.07; 12.73; 12.19
23.2; 3.46; 59.77
42.26; 20.34; 1.42; 42.21; 46.63
23.40; 20.43; 0.19; 5.15; 25.42
7.14; 39.05; 2.71; 32.12; 65.25
0.41; 34.45; 2.27; 0.66; 68.89
9.32; 13.55; 13.57; 32.6; 25.49
68.52; 16.23; 4.01; 32.77; 11.92

Page 78

3 places to the left
4 places to the left

A. 4.75 / 0.65 / 0.02391
B. 0.475 / 0.039 / 0.0744
C. 0.0475 / 0.0853 / 0.00532
D. 0.000475 / 0.00097 / 0.00014

3 places to the right

E. 475.0 / 265.00 / 4560.00
F. 4750.0 / 54,930.00 / 34.490
G. 47,500.0 / 76.120 / 97.6300
H. 475,000.0 / 3570.0 / 9310.000
I. 580.0 / 0.71 / 53.20
J. 0.224 / 1026 / 0.0043

Page 79

A. 0.29	9.1	0.4	0.4	9.7
B. 1.4	0.53	10.4	0.71	3.13
C. 0.26	0.6	0.368	0.2	0.024
D. 0.302	0.36	0.8	0.24	4.1
E. 0.406	0.327	0.802	0.250	2.34

Page 80

3.05, 6.5, .056, 1.007, 12, 80
5.9, 1384, 3.6, 8.1, 3.1
2.65, .84, 37.2, 3.4, 2.09, 35
REMOVE THE FIRST LETTER

Page 81

$37.99	$19.59	$2.67	$25.31	$16.74
$15.88	$12.97	$13.77	$63.35	$61.37
$16.32	$90.08	$58.63	$5.82	$15.36
$2.19	$24.67	$44.12	$5.46	$9.36
$3.54	$2.85	$38.77	$59.32	$69.88

Page 82

A. $46.90 – 47, $42.90 – 42, $17.99 – 18, $33.00 – 33

B. $37.16 – 37, $59.21 – 59, $1195.21 – 1195, $42.19 – 43

C. $63.10 – 63, $52.27 – 52, $17.39 – 18, $29.08 – 30

Page 83

1. 3 yards
2. $11.37
3. 1/2 yard, 63¢
4. 8 eyes, 60¢
5. $12.60, $3.15
6. $15.40
7. No
8. Yes
9. 1/4 yard
10. 1 1/8 yards

Page 84

1. $54.67
2. $49.05
3. $62.75
4. $6.75
5. $38.74
6. $121.49
7. $9.45
8. $46.57
9. $47.43
10. $58.50

Page 85

1. a. 40, b. 2, c. 50
2. 12
3. 85¢
4. $1.50
5. 15¢
6. 15¢
7. $1.25
8. 9¢
9. $104.80
10. $84.80
11. $4.42

Page 86

16 > 15
30 = 30
6 = 6; 13 < 15; 12 < 13
63 < 64; 19 > 10; 4 = 4
11 > 9; 56 > 54; 14 < 17
44 = 44; 10 > 9; 38 = 38
23 = 23; 13 = 13; 9 > 7
48 = 48; 24 > 23; 12 < 15

Page 87

1. <	10. =	19. >	28. =
2. >	11. >	20. =	29. =
3. =	12. >	21. >	30. =
4. <	13. >	22. >	31. >
5. >	14. =	23. =	32. =
6. <	15. <	24. =	33. <
7. =	16. =	25. =	34. =
8. =	17. >	26. <	35. <
9. <	18. <	27. <	36. =

Page 88

1. 8 min.
2. 3 hr. 45 min.
3. 2 centuries
4. 112; yes
5. 180 sec.
6. 13 wk. 1 d.
7. 3 d. 3 hr.
8. 1 yr. 10 wk. 4 d.
9. a. 120, b. 520, c. 3650
10. 10 hr. 55 min.

Page 89

1. 2 hrs. 35 min
2. 17 min
3. 8:25 A.M.
4. 10:35 A.M.
5. 3:20 P.M.
6. 11:12 A.M. – 10:29 A.M.
7. 11 P.M.
8. 9:50 A.M. – Wednesday
9. 7.5 hours
10. 1/3   1/4
    3/4   1/6
    2/3   1/2

Page 90

Length	Capacity
10 m	5 mi
30 mm	1 l
24 cm	4 kl
18 cm	3 l
12 cm	180 ml
90 cm	15 l

Weight	Temperature
14 g	48° C
270 g	5° C
46 kg	40° C
130 mg	-4° C
145 g	80° C
60 g	5° C

Page 91

100 yards	5 miles
9 inches	6 feet
4 yards	17 inches
6 inches	3 miles
8 inches	28 inches
4 feet	9 feet

in	yd
ft	ft
mi	in
in	ft
mi	yd
yd	mi

Page 92

1. 1 ft. 7 in.
2. 2 yd. 2 ft.
3. 1 mi. 1320 ft.
4. 1 yd. 1 ft. 6 in.
5. length: 26 cm 7 mm, width: 20 cm 1 mm
6. length: 27 cm 9 mm, width: 21 cm 6 mm
7. length: 1 cm 2 mm, width: 1 cm 5 mm
8. 1 m 55 cm

Page 93

1. 3 lb.
2. 15 lb.
3. 22 oz.
4. 24 oz.
5. 13,000 lb.
6. 12 tn.
7. 2 g 208 mg
8. 30,000 g
9. 110 kg
10. 995 g
11. 1900 lb.; 1 tn.
12. 454,000 mg
13. 226 g
14. 283,000 mg
15. 40 oz.
16. 238,000 lb.

Page 94

1. a. 180°, b. 100°
2. a. 67° F, b. 113° F
3. a. 37° C, b. 63° C
4. 7° F
5. 4° C
6. a. 38° F, b. 21° C
7. a. 72° F, b. 40° C
8. 109° F
9. 43° C

Page 95

250 yd	190 mi
56 in	120 in or 10 ft
150 ft or 50 yd	72 in or 6 ft

Page 96

1. a. 18 ft., b. 18 sq. ft.
2. a. 144 in., b. 1296 sq. in.
3. a. 12 ft., b. 8 sq. ft.
4. a. 156 in., b. 1440 sq. in.
5. a. 244 ft., b. 3600 sq. ft.
6. a. 12 sq. yd., b. 14 yd., c. 42 ft.
7. a. 64 in., b. 252 sq. in.
8. a. 44 in., b. 120 sq. in.
9. a. 108 in., b. 648 sq. in.
10. a. 10 ft., b. 4 sq. ft.

Page 97

1. chocolate
2. 4
3. 36
1. 45
2. 10%
3. 10
1. 6, 10
2. 50
3. 80%
1. 15%
2. 15
3. 20%

Page 98

square	hexagon
triangle	octagon

Page 99

1. Indianapolis - 49°, Minneapolis - 62°
2. Indianapolis - 72°, Minneapolis - 68°/4°
3. Minneapolis - 45°, Indianapolis - 52°/7°
4. Boston - 74°, Des Moines - 76°
5. Des Moines - 8°
6. Des Moines - 50°, Boston - 52°/2°
7. September - 65°

Page 100

Page 101

Page 102

1. 8 feet
2. 7 trucks
3. $42.12
4. 1600 trees
5. Not enough information.
6. 1089 trees
7. 10 hours
8. 1000 for $150
9. $162.00
10. 7 feet

Page 103

1. $2.25
2. $540
3. $3.35
4. $11.85
5. $21.75

Page 104

1. 182 points
2. $1,155
3. 46 customers
4. $165
5. $276

Page 105

1. 31 rocks
2. 450 baseball cards
3. $35
4. 86 cars
5. 168 stickers
6. 44 worms

Page 106

1. 725 cows
2. 490 cows were sold
3. 63 steaks
4. 530 pounds of meat
5. 235 cows were left

Page 107

1. 17 days
2. 630 pounds of food
3. 1,268 feet
4. 15 boys
5. 1,537 pieces of dessert

Page 108

1. 70 bullfrogs
2. 1,079 pounds
3. 7 eggs
4. 22 minutes
5. 195 grams
6. 70 million years

Page 109

1. 56 sheets of plywood
2. 8 more trusses
3. $40,000
4. 134 studs
5. 72 studs

Page 110

1. $244
2. 756 miles
3. $12.52
4. 6 minutes
5. 61 parakeets
6. $765

Page 111

1. 2,885 feet
2. 2,801 feet
3. $5
4. 343 lbs.
5. $475

Page 112

1. $10,800
2. 2-cent Jackson
3. $102.50
4. unused 24-cent Washington
5. 12

Page 113

1. $705
2. 111 men
3. 38 days
4. 18 pounds of venison
5. $1,200

Page 114

1. 383 yards
2. 64 yards
3. 182
4. 9
5. 525 yards

Page 115

1. 28 inches
2. 13 degrees
3. 91 crickets
4. 70 crickets
5. 26 lizards
6. 16 degrees

Page 116

1. 148 more pages
2. $23
3. $96
4. $16.95
5. $7.25

Page 117

1. 11 degrees
2. $16
3. 4 hours
4. 56 lemons
5. 42 cups

Page 118

1. 208 graves
2. $356
3. 242 cattle
4. 76 cents
5. 72 pies

Page 119

1. 38
2. 38
3. 64
4. 36
5. 57
6. 81

Page 120

1. K causes the 9 to be a constant addend.
2. 114 is not divisible by 9.
3. 4 is the constant addend.
4. 9 is the constant addend.
5. 8
6. 7 + K =
7. 47
8. Yes. 82-5+77 and 77 is divisible by 7.
9. No. 90-5 = 85 and 85 is not divisible by 7.
10. 15 times; Add 110-5 = 105 and 105 ÷7 = 15.

Page 121

1. 310
2. 340
3. 330
4. 51
5. 84
6. 18
7. 35
8. 182
9. 182
10. 500
11. 216

Page 122

1. 16 servings
2. $39.00
3. 12 people
4. $3.25
5. 8-16 oz. bottles, 1¢ per oz.
6. $3.19
7. dough - 18¢, sauce - 78¢, pepperoni - $1.19, cheese - $1.50, Total cost - $3.65
8. $1.38